IMPROVE YOUR GAME

100 Chess Puzzles

PAUL LAMFORD

Chameleon Books

First published in 1999 by Chameleon Books,
an imprint of André Deutsch Ltd,
76 Dean Street London W1V 5HA
(www.vci.co.uk)

The right of Paul Lamford to be identified as the Author of this Work
has been asserted by him in accordance with the Copyright Design
and Patents Act 1988

Typeset by Games and Pastimes Consultancy
8 Arbor Court London N16 0QU. Tel/Fax: (0181) 809 3063

British Library Cataloguing in Publication Data
Data available

ISBN 0 233 99713 X

Printed and bound in Great Britain by
MPG Books Ltd, Bodmin, Cornwall

Contents

Acknowledgements

The author would like to thank John Roycroft for checking sources. The author takes full responsibility for any errors and would welcome comments sent to himat gampas@aol.com.

To Bob Wade, OBE, who has done so much for British chess

Simple Combinations

1

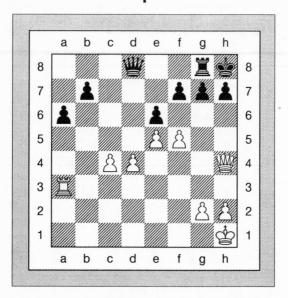

White to move

White's pawns are under pressure in the above position. Should White exchange queens, retreat his queen, or play something else?

HINT
**The black king is boxed in at the edge of the board
which suggests a sacrifice**

Solutions are on the following page

2

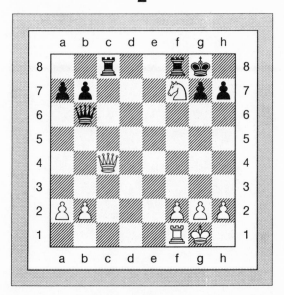

White to move

White can force a draw here by 1 ♘h6++ ♚h8 2 ♘f7+ ♚g8 3 ♘h6++. Does either side have anything better?

HINT
Here you need to deprive the black king of a flight square by means of a sacrifice

---

Solutions are on the following page

3

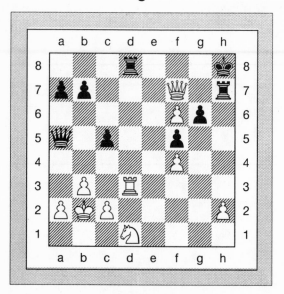

White to move

Black is the exchange up here and seems to be defending White's attack. How does White win quickly?

HINT
The rook on h7 is defending the mate on g7 at the moment. Does that suggest White's winning move?

Solution to Puzzle 1

White wins prettily by 1 ♕xh7+ ♔xh7 (a forced move) 2 ♖h3+ ♕h4 (again the only move) 3 ♖xh4 mate (diagram).

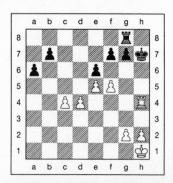

4

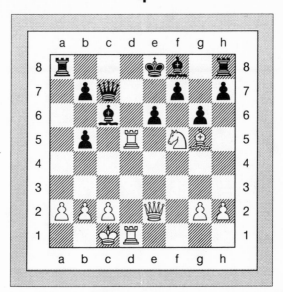

White to move

White can win Black's queen here by 1 ♖d8+ ♖xd8 2 ♖xd8+ ♕xd8 3 ♗xd8. Does White have anything stronger?

HINT
If Black's queen could be deflected from the defence of d8 White could force mate there. Any ideas?

Solution to Puzzle 2
White can force checkmate by 1 ♘h6++ ♔h8 2 ♕g8+ ♖xg8 (only move) 3 ♘f7 mate (diagram). This is known as smothered mate.

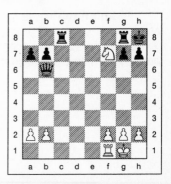

5

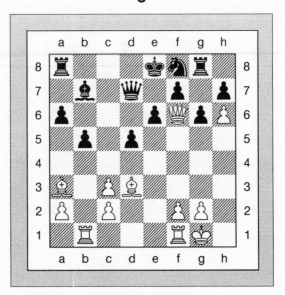

White to move

Black is dangerously weak on the dark squares in this position but seems to have everything covered. How does White win?

HINT
The white pawn on h6 plays a part and White wins with an unusual queen move

---

Solution to Puzzle 3

White forces mate by 1 ♖h3 ♖xh3 2 ♕g7 mate (diagram). A simple example of deflection.

6

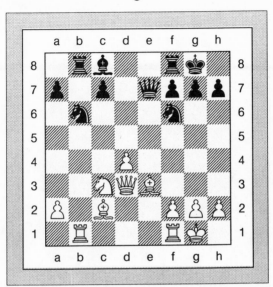

White to move

White has the more active position here; but how does he force a quick victory?

HINT
The white bishop and queen lining up against the h7 square suggest a way to proceed

---

Solution to Puzzle 4

The best move is 1 ♕e5! and if 1 ... ♕xe5 2 ♖d8+ ♖xd8 3 ♖xd8 mate (diagram). If the black queen moves, White plays 2 ♖d8+ ♖xd8 3 ♖xd8+ ♕xd8 4 ♗xd8 and the rook on h8 is also attacked.

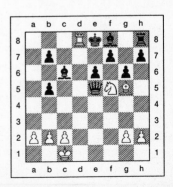

7

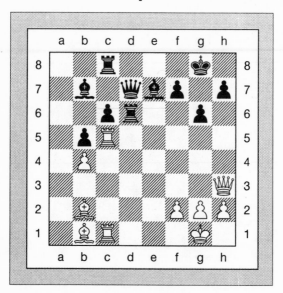

White to move

White has some pressure down the c-file here, but Black is hoping to exchange queens to ease his position. What should White play?

HINT
**The powerful white bishops pointing at the
black king suggest a combination**

Solution to Puzzle 5

White wins material by 1 ♕g7! attacking the rook. Black cannot defend it and 1 ... ♖xg7 2 hxg7 (diagram) wins with the twin threats of promoting on f8 or g8.

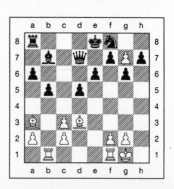

8

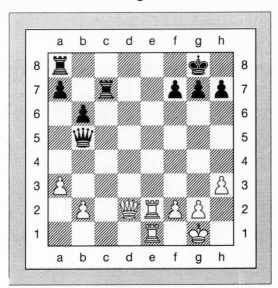

White to move

Material is equal here but White's pieces are better co-ordinated. How does White win quickly?

> **HINT**
> **A black king with three unmoved pawns in front of it can sometime be vulnerable to a back-rank mate**

Solution to Puzzle 6

White wins immediately with 1 ♖xb6! axb6 (1 ... ♖xb6 or 1 ... cxb6 are met by the same reply) 2 ♘d5! (attacking the queen and threatening ♘xf6+) 2 ... ♘xd5 3 ♕xh7 mate (diagram).

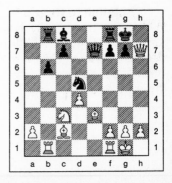

9

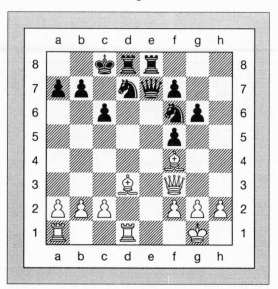

White to move

Black looks to have a solid position here, but there is one weakness; can you spot how White wins quickly?

HINT
Black's king does not have a legal move at present; how can White take advantage of this?

Solution to Puzzle 7
White forces mate by 1 ♕xh7+ ♔xh7 (1 ... ♔f8 2 ♕h8 mate) 2 ♖h5+ ♔g8 3 ♖h8 mate (diagram).

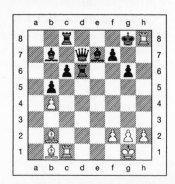

10

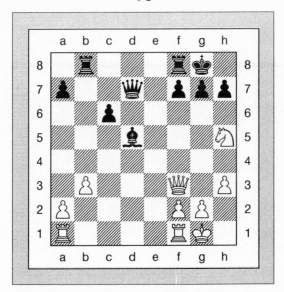

White to move

White's queen is attacked here and Black looks to have a good position. However White can win material tactically. How?

HINT
The fork 1 ♘f6+ doesn't lead anywhere
but there is an idea based on this theme

Solution to Puzzle 8

White can win material by 1 ♕d5! ♕xd5 (otherwise White plays ♕xa8+; 1 ... ♕c6 2 ♕xc6 ♖xc6 3 ♖e8+ forces mate similarly) 2 ♖e8+ ♖xe8 3 ♖xe8 mate (diagram)

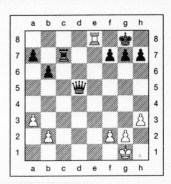

Tactical Tricks

11

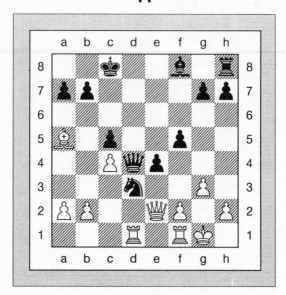

White to move

Black has a pawn for the exchange here and the knight on d3 looks strong; however White has a quick tactical win. How?

HINT
Black's bank rank is a bit weak;
is there any way to exploit this?

Solution to Puzzle 9

White forces mate by 1 ♕xc6+ bxc6 2 ♗a6 mate (diagram).

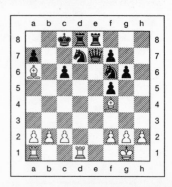

12

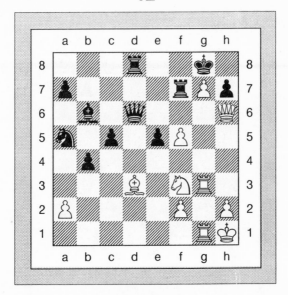

White to move

White has a strong attack here but Black is planning to exchange queens. How can White force a quick win?

HINT
If 1 f6, then 1 ... ♕xd3 defends the weak h7 square;
does this suggest a sacrifice?

Solution to Puzzle 10
White wins the exchange and a pawn by 1 ♕f6! (threatening 2 ♕xg7 mate) 1 ... gxf6 2 ♘xf6+ ♔g7 3 ♘xd7 forking the black rooks (diagram).

13

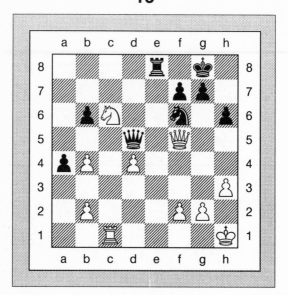

White to move

World Champion Anatoly Karpov overlooked the win here; can you do better and work out how White wins quickly?

HINT
There are some tactical possibilities
based on the weak back rank

Solution to Puzzle 11
White wins material by 1 ♖xd3 ♕xd3 (1 ... exd3 2 ♕e8+ forces mate) 2 ♖d1! pinning the queen against the back rank. If 2 ... ♕xe2 3 ♖d8 mate (diagram) so Black has to give up his queen.

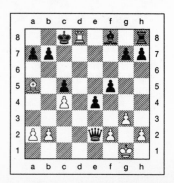

14

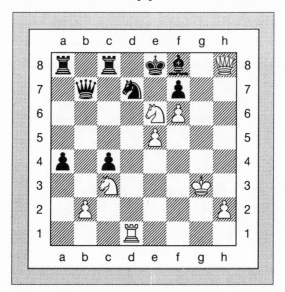

White to move

White recovered some of the sacrificed material here by 1 ♘g7+ ♚d8 2 ♛xf8+. How could he have won quickly?

HINT
The black king has no flight squares at present; does this suggest an alternative move?

Solution to Puzzle 12

White wins brilliantly by 1 ♛xh7+ ♚xh7 2 f6+ ♚g8 (2 ... ♛xd3 3 ♖h3+ forces mate) 3 ♗h7+! ♚xh7 4 ♖h3+ ♚g8 5 ♖h8 mate (diagram).

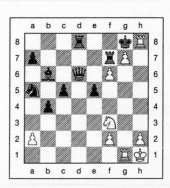

15

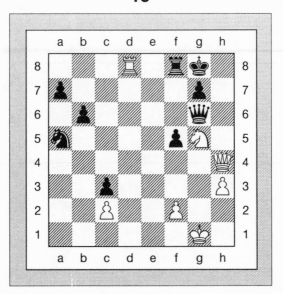

White to move

White repeated moves here with 1 ♖d6 ♖f6 2 ♖d8+ ♖f8. Could either side have done better?

HINT
Again the black king does not have any flight squares; how can you exploit that?

Solution to Puzzle 13

White wins material by 1 ♘e7+ ♖xe7 (otherwise Black loses his queen) 2 ♖c8+ ♖e8 3 ♖xe8+ ♘xe8 4 ♕xd5 (diagram). A surprising oversight by both Karpov and his strong opponent Lubosh Kavalek.

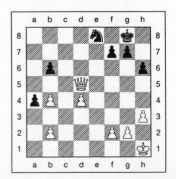

16

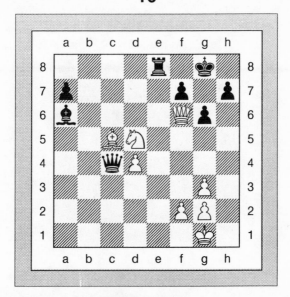

White to move

Black is very weak on the dark squares here; how can White exploit this to win quickly?

HINT
The g7 square is a particularly vulnerable point in Black's position. Which move exploits that?

Solution to Puzzle 14
White can force checkmate by 1 ♕xf8+ ♘xf8 2 ♘g7 mate (diagram). This was missed in the game and White won after a long struggle.

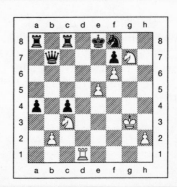

17

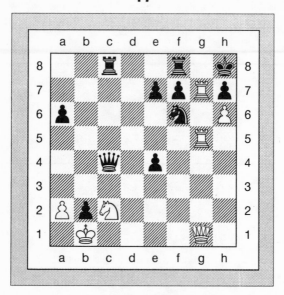

White to move

White has pressure down the g-file here, but Black is threatening mate in one with ... ♕xc2. How does White win?

HINT
What is needed is an aggressive move that also meets the threat of mate

---

Solution to Puzzle 15

White wins simply by 1 ♕h8+ ♔xh8 2 ♖xf8 mate (diagram). This was overlooked by a strong master, although he was short of time.

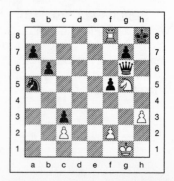

18

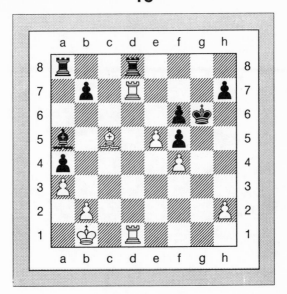

White to move

Even in the endgame, tactics can play a part. How does White force victory?

HINT
The black king is looking a bit exposed;
is there any way of exploiting this?

Solution to Puzzle 16

White can force a quick mate by 1 ♗f8! ♕c1+ 2 ♔h2 (diagram) and Black is mated after 2 ... ♖xf8 2 ♘e7 or 2 ... ♔xf8 3 ♕h8. 1 ♘e7+ instead allows 1 ... ♖xe7 2 ♕xe7 ♕c1+ 3 ♔h2 ♕h6+ with a drawn position.

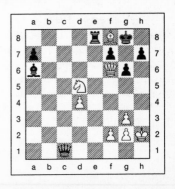

19

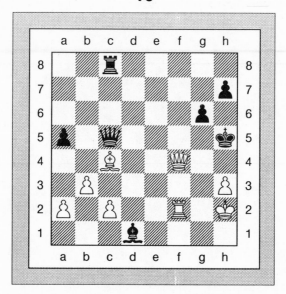

White to move

White is a pawn up with a long-term win, but how can he force immediate resignation?

HINT
**The black king is extremely exposed on h5;
what is the best way to exploit this?**

Solution to Puzzle 17

White wins by 1 ♖c5! ♛xc5 (1 ... ♖xc5 leads to the same finish) 2 ♖xh7+! ♚xh7 (2 ... ♞xh7 meets the same reply) 3 ♛g7 mate (diagram). Black has to give up his queen after the first move, but that is hopeless.

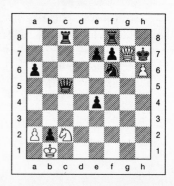

20

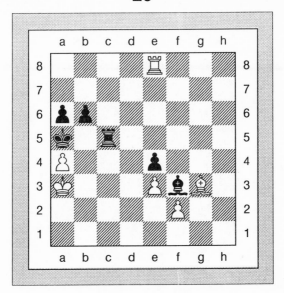

White to move

Opposite-coloured bishops normally lead to a draw, but here White has a surprising win; what is it?

HINT
Black is threatening ... ♖c3+; curiously one way of stopping it is decisive

---

Solution to Puzzle 18

White forces mate by 1 ♖g1+ ♔h6 (1 ... ♔h5 2 ♖xh7 mate) 2 ♗f8+! (deflecting the black rook) 2 ... ♖xf8 3 ♖d3 (diagram) and Black can only postpone the mate on h3.

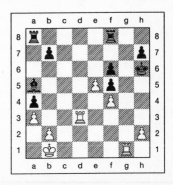

Mating Attacks

21

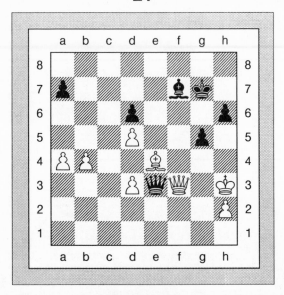

Black to move

Black seems to be struggling to draw here, but surprisingly he has a fairly quick win. What should he play?

HINT
The white king at the edge of the board is vulnerable to some surprise tactics

---

Solution to Puzzle 19
White wins material or mates after 1 ♖e2! ♗xe2 (otherwise White wins the queen by 2 ♖e5+) 2 ♗xe2 mate (diagram).

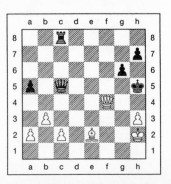

22

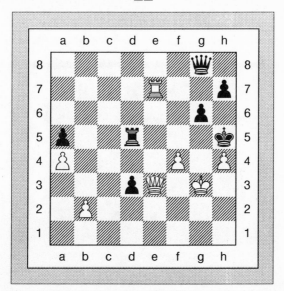

White to move

Black's passed pawn looks strong here, but White has an immediate forced win. What should he play?

HINT
The black king is the more exposed here;
how does White exploit this?

Solution to Puzzle 20

Paradoxically White wins by forcing the exchange of rooks with 1 ♖e5! ♖xe5 2 ♗xe5 b5 (the only way to stop ♗c3 mate) 3 ♗c7 mate (diagram). Black cannot leave his rook on c5 either as 1 ... ♗moves allows 2 ♖xc5+ bxc5 3 ♗c7 mate.

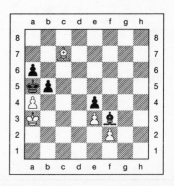

23

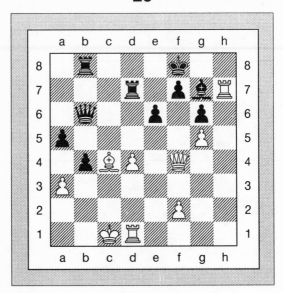

White to move

A wild position in which both sides have threats. How does White get in first?

HINT
The sacrifice on g7 looks attractive, but Black does not have to accept it. Maybe you should look further?

Solution to Puzzle 21

Black wins by 1 ... g4+ (a fork ...) 2 ♔xg4 ♗h5+ (... and a deflection) 3 ♔xh5 ♕g5 mate (diagram). The alternative is for White to give up his queen.

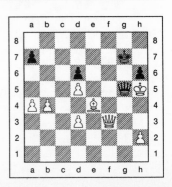

24

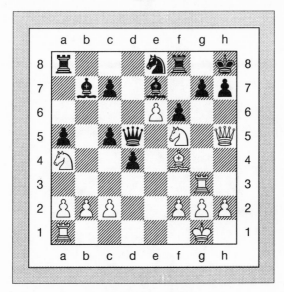

White to move

White has a an aggressive position here and it is no surprise that he has a winning combination. What is it?

HINT
Black is short of squares for his king again;
what does that suggest?

Solution to Puzzle 22

White can force mate by 1 ♕e6! ♕xe6 2 ♖xh7 mate (diagram). Other queen moves also lead to a quick mate. In the game White played 1 ♖xh7+ ♕xh7 2 ♕f3+ ♔h6 3 ♕xd5 but Black managed to draw.

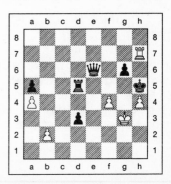

25

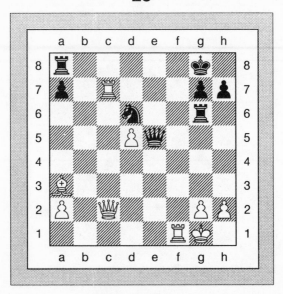

White to move

White's pieces are more active here, but how does he force a quick win?

HINT
Black is a bit weak on the back rank;
does that give you any ideas?

Solution to Puzzle 23

White wins by 1 ♕f6 (not 1 ♖xg7 ♖c8 with strong threats) 1 ... ♗xf6 (if 1 ... bxa3 now, 2 ♕xg7+ ♔e8 3 ♖h8+ ♔e7 4 ♕f6+ ♔d6 5 ♕e5+ and 6 ♖xb8 is decisive) 2 gxf6 ♔g8 3 ♖dh1 (diagram) and Black cannot prevent ♖h8 mate.

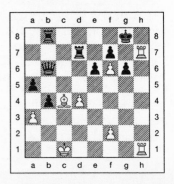

26

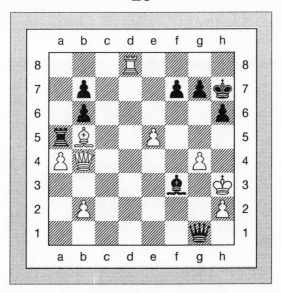

White to move

The advantage of the move is crucial here as Black has strong mating threats of his own. How does White get in first?

HINT
In view of Black's threats, White might have
to win with a series of checks

Solution to Puzzle 24
White forces mate by 1 ♕xh7+ ♚xh7 2 ♖h3+ ♚g6 (2 ... ♚g8 is met by the same reply) 3 ♘xe7 mate (diagram).

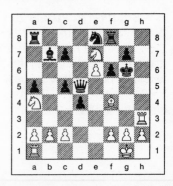

27

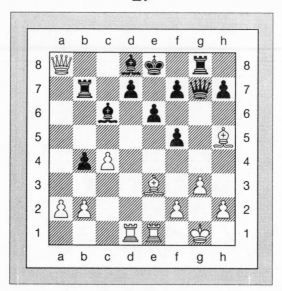

White to move

White's rooks and bishops look menacing here. What sequence of moves forces victory?

HINT
Exploiting the pins on the d8 bishop and the f-pawn is the key here; what is the right order of moves?

Solution to Puzzle 25
White forces a quick mate by 1 ♖c8+ ♖xc8 (1 ... ♛e8 stops mate at ruinous material loss) 2 ♛xc8+ ♘xc8 (or 2 ... ♛e8 3 ♛xe8+ ♘xe8 4 ♖f8 mate) 3 ♖f8 mate (diagram)

28

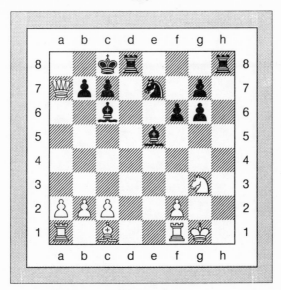

White to move

Black has sacrificed his queen here for only a bishop. How should he continue his attack?

HINT
Black must act quickly before White brings his queen back to the defence. A sacrifice is in order.

Solution to Puzzle 26

White forces mate by 1 ♗d3+ g6 2 ♖h8+ ♔xh8 3 ♕f8+ ♔h7 4 ♕xf7+ ♔h8 5 ♕f8+ ♔h7 6 ♗xg6+! ♔xg6 7 ♕g8 mate (diagram). A model mate in which no escape square is covered more than once!

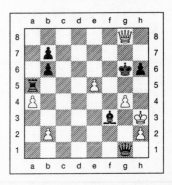

29

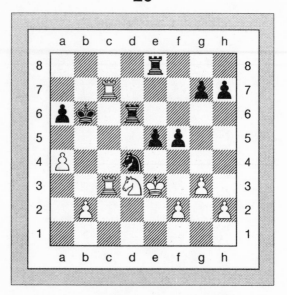

White to move

White could capture Black's g-pawn and have a clear advantage; however he has a much better way of winning. What is it?

HINT
Again the black king is vulnerable to attack;
what sequence of move. How do we corner him?

Solution to Puzzle 27

White wins by 1 ♗b6 ♖xb6 (1 ... ♕f6 2 ♖xe6+ dxe6 3 ♖xd8+ mates; 1 ... ♔e7 2 ♗c5+ d6 3 ♗xd6+ ♔e8 4 ♗c7 mates) 2 ♖xe6+! dxe6 (or 2 ... ♔f8 3 ♕xd8 mate) 3 ♕xd8 mate (diagram).

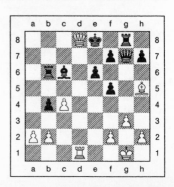

30

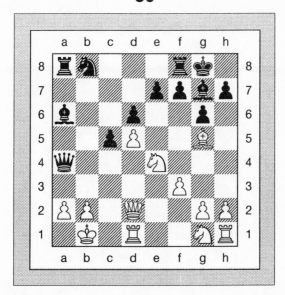

Black to move

White seems under pressure here but how does Black unleash a long combination that forces mate?

HINT
Black needs to break down the pawn barrier around White's king and drag him into the open

---

Solution to Puzzle 28
White missed a beautiful forced mate by 1 ... ♖h1+! 2 ♘xh1 ♗h2+ 3 ♔xh2 ♖h8+ 4 ♔g3 (4 ♔g1 ♖xh1 mate) 4 ... ♘f5+ 5 ♔g4 (or 5 ♔f4) 5 ... ♖h4 mate (diagram).

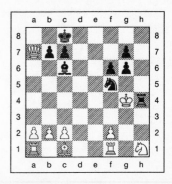

Opening Traps

31

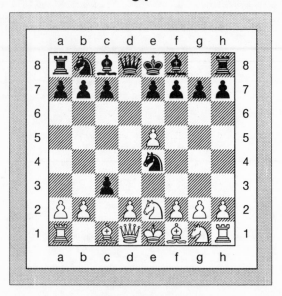

White to move

Black has just captured on c3 with a pawn on d4. Is this a cunning trap or a blunder and what should White play?

HINT
After White wins the piece look out for Black's
counter-attack using his pawn at c3

Solution to Puzzle 29

White wins by 1 a5+ ♔xa5 (1 ... ♔b5 2 ♖7c5+ forces mate) 2 ♖b7 (threatening ♖a3 mate) 2 ... f4+ 3 ♔e4 ♘b5 (seemingly meeting the threat) 4 ♖a3+! ♘xa3 5 b4+ ♔a4 6 ♘c5 mate (diagram).

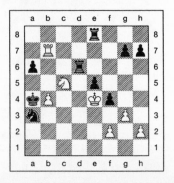

32

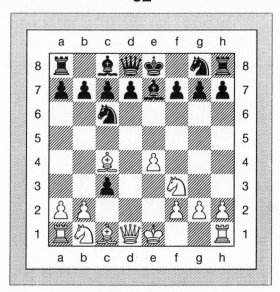

White to move

Again Black has just captured on c3. Can White win material or does Black have a resource?

HINT
White's first move is not hard to find; but you need to keep looking for Black's defence

---

Solution to Puzzle 30

Black forced mate by 1 ... ♛xa2+ 2 ♔xa2 ♗d3+ 3 ♔b3 c4+ 4 ♔b4 ♞a6+ (*Fritz* points out that 4 ... ♞c6+ mates more quickly) 5 ♔b5 (5 ♔a4 ♞c5++ 6 ♔b5 ♖fb8+ 7 ♔c6 ♖a6+ soon mates) 5 ... ♖fb8+ 6 ♔c6 ♖c8+ 7 ♔b7 (7 ♔b5 ♞c7+ soon mates too) 7 ... ♖c7+! ♔xa8 ♗d4 and White cannot stop ... ♖a7 mate (diagram). A beautiful king hunt.

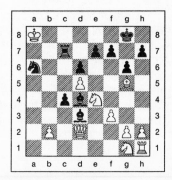

33

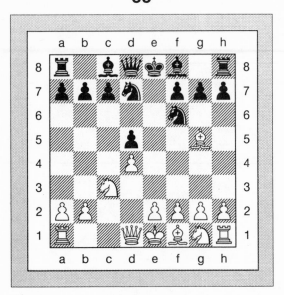

White to move

It looks tempting to capture the d5 pawn here; has Black blundered or is it a trap?

> **HINT**
> **Never assume a piece pinned**
> **against the queen can't move**

Solution to Puzzle 31

It looks like White can win a piece with a fork by 1 ♕a4+ but after 1 ... ♘d7 2 ♕xe4 ♘c5! Black recovers the material with interest, e.g. 3 ♕f3 ♘d3+ 4 ♔d1 cxb2 winning back the piece (diagram). White should just recapture with 1 bxc3.

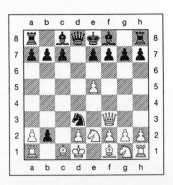

34

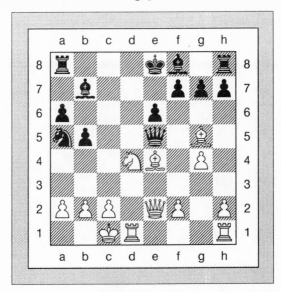

White to move

Black has just played ... ♕e5 attacking both white bishops; does this win material or does White have a resource.

> **HINT**
> **The black king has no flight squares**
> **and this suggests a sacrifice**

Solution to Puzzle 32

White cannot win material and the position is about level. After 1 ♕d5 (threatening mate) 1 ...♘h6 2 ♗xh6 0-0 Black recovers his piece because 3 ♗c1 allows 3 ... ♘b4 4 ♕d1 (otherwise 4 ... ♘c2+) 4 ... c2! (diagram). Black remains a pawn up. 3 ♗xg7 ♔xg7 4 ♘xc3 is best.

35

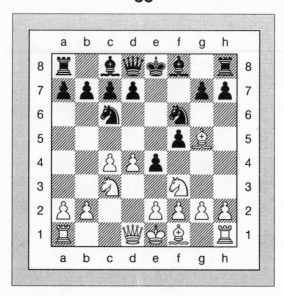

White to move

White provoked some exchanges here with 1 d5 exf3 2 dxc6
Was this a good or a bad idea?

> **HINT**
> **After the initial exchanges Black can win a pawn by
> a surprising resource. What is it?**

Solution to Puzzle 33

White should ignore the d-pawn and just carry on with developing moves. 1 ♘xd5? allows 1 ... ♘xd5 2 ♗xd8 ♗b4+ 3 ♕d2 ♔xd8 and Black will emerge a piece to the good (diagram).

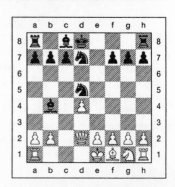

36

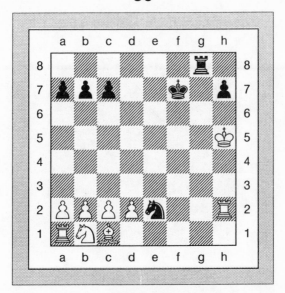

Black to move

Yes, this is a position from opening theory; Black is to play and is a rook and bishop down. How should he continue?

HINT
It looks like Black has a draw by perpetual check with the knight. Does he have anything more?

Solution to Puzzle 34

White has a very strong move 1 ♘xe6! ♕xe6 (1 … ♕xe4 2 ♕xe4 ♗xe4 3 ♘c7 mate; 1 … fxe6 2 ♗g6+ wins the queen; 1 … ♗xe4 2 ♕xe4 ♕xe4 3 ♘c7 mate; 1 … ♗e7 is about the only move but 2 ♕d2 is winning easily) 2 ♗f5! ♕xe2 3 ♗d7 mate (diagram).

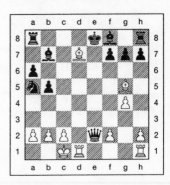

37

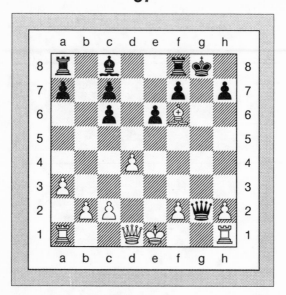

White to move

White looks in trouble here because 1 ♖f1 is met by 1 ... ♗a6.
However, White has something much stronger. What?

HINT
The black king on the open file looks vulnerable;
how does White get at him?

Solution to Puzzle 35
Black continues 2 ... fxg2 3
cxd7+? (after 3 ♗xg2 bxc6 White
is a pawn down) 3 ... ♘xd7!
(diagram) and White must,
surprisingly, lose a piece. Oddly,
three masters have fallen for this
trap.

38

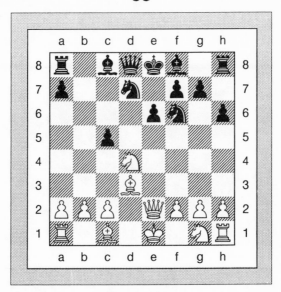

White to move

Black has just played ... c5 attacking the white knight but this was a blunder. How does White win material?

HINT
A sacrifice on e6 suggests itself, but that doesn't work at present; how can White prepare it?

Solution to Puzzle 36

Black can force mate with 1 ... ♘f4+ 2 ♔h6 (2 ♔h4 h5! forces mate) 2 ... ♖g6+ 3 ♔xh7 ♖g7+ 4 ♔h6 ♔g8 (diagram) and White has no defence against ... ♖g6 mate.

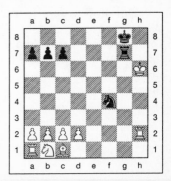

39

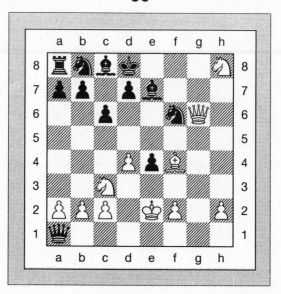

White to move

Black has been grabbing material here at the expense of his development. How can he be punished?

HINT
Look back at Puzzle 2;
the finish is somewhat similar

Solution to Puzzle 37
White wins immediately with 1 ♕f3! ♕xf3 2 ♖g1+ (diagram) forcing mate. 1 ... ♕g6 2 0-0-0! threatening ♖g1 also wins the queen.

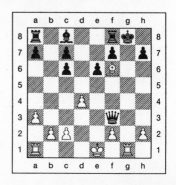

40

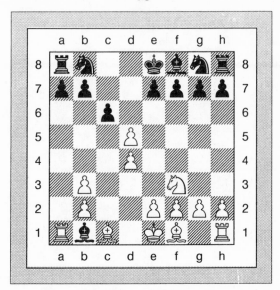

White to move

Black hopes to have a solid position here after 1 ♖xb1 cxd5. What tactical trick does White have?

> **HINT**
> **The pawn on d5 can be used here;**
> **but 1 dxc6 is met by 1 … ♗e4, or is it?**

Solution to Puzzle 38

White wins the black queen by 1 ♘c6 ♛c7 (1 … ♛b6 meets the same reply) 2 ♕xe6+ fxe6 3 ♗g6 mate (diagram).

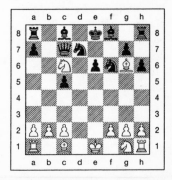

Turning the Tables

41

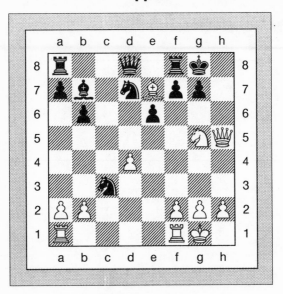

Black to move

Black's queen, rook and knight are *en prise* here and mate in one is threatened. How did Black win?

HINT
Sometimes attack is the best form of defence.
What tactical resource had White overlooked?

Solution to Puzzle 39
White can force mate by 1 ♘f7+ ♚e8 2 ♘d6+ ♚d8 3 ♕e8+! ♘xe8 (3 ... ♚c7 4 ♕xc8+ ♚b6 5 ♕xb7+ ♚a5 6 ♘c4 mate) 4 ♘f7 mate (diagram).

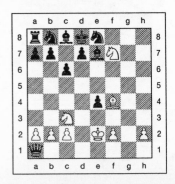

42

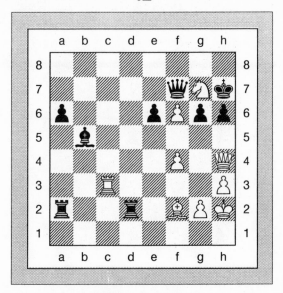

White to move

White seems in deep trouble here with Black's rooks on the seventh rank. How does he launch a winning counter-attack?

HINT
The Black king look secure, but White has a way of developing unstoppable threats. How?

Solution to Puzzle 40

White should play 1 dxc6, winning a pawn, as 1 ... ♗e4 is met by the clever 2 ♖xa7! ♖xa7 2 c7 (diagram) and White's pawn promotes.

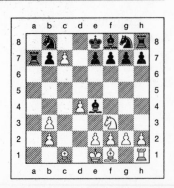

43

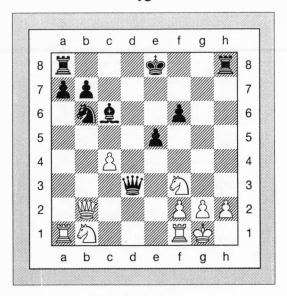

White to move

White continued 1 ♕xb6 here, expecting to win material after 1 ...
axb6 2 ♖xa8+ and 3 ♖xh8. What had he missed?

HINT
Black has a counter-attack of his own,
without capturing White's queen. What is it?

Solution to Puzzle 41
Black wins by 1 ... ♘e2+ 2 ♔h1
♗xg2+ 3 ♔xg2 ♘f4+ 4 ♔h1
♘xh5 5 ♗xd8 ♖exd8 (diagram)
and Black is a piece up.

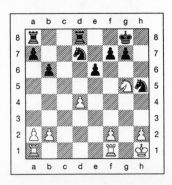

44

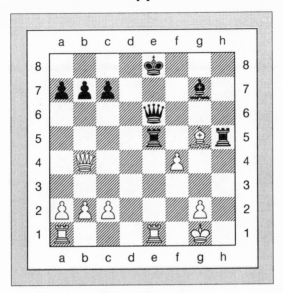

White to move

Black seems to be in trouble with his rook attacked and a potential pin on the e-file. What winning trick did he have?

HINT
**The white king is somewhat exposed as well;
how did Black exploit that?**

Solution to Puzzle 42
In the game White resigned in the above diagram, but he wins by 1 ♖c8! ♖xf2 2 ♕xh6+! ♔xh6 3 ♖h8 mate (diagram). Black has no reasonable defence to the threat (1 ... h5 2 ♕g5 or 1 ... g5 2 hxg5).

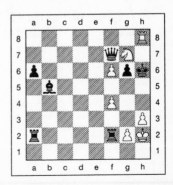

45

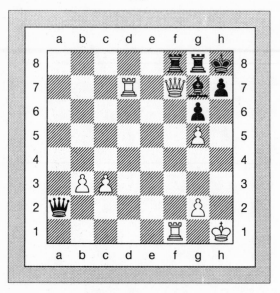

White to move

White seems in desperate trouble here, a piece down and with his queen attacked. What drawing resource does he have?

HINT
Two rooks on the seventh rank can create very strong threats; how does White achieve that?

Solution to Puzzle 43

1 ♕xb6 is met by 1 ... ♕xf3! 2 gxf3 ♖g8+ 3 ♔h1 ♗xf3 mate (diagram).

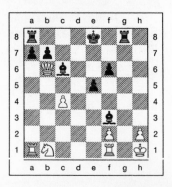

46

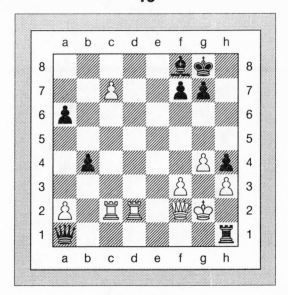

White to move

Black cannot stop the pawn on c7 here, but he has a tactical trick which forces a draw. What is it?

HINT
White seems to have all the threats covered;
how can Black force perpetual check?

Solution to Puzzle 44
Black won by 1 ... ♖xe1+ 2 ♖xe1 ♗d4+! 3 ♔f1 (or 3 ♕xd4 ♕xe1 mate) 3 ... ♖h1 mate (diagram).

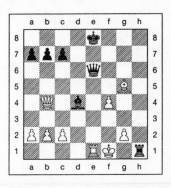

47

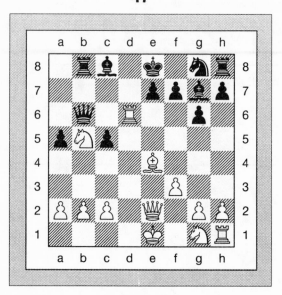

Black to move

Black's queen is trapped here, and, calculating 1 ... exd6 2 ♗c6+
with mate on e8, he resigned. What had he missed?

HINT
**Black has an unexpected trick, creating a flight
square for his king. What is it?**

Solution to Puzzle 45
White forces a draw by 1 ♕xg7+!
♖xg7 2 ♖xf8+ ♖g8 3 ♖ff7
(diagram). Black cannot avoid a
draw by perpetual check from the
rooks.

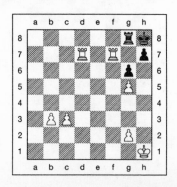

48

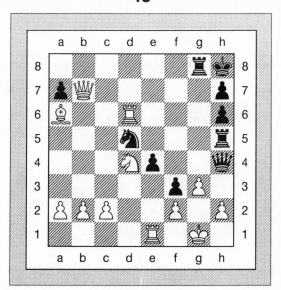

White to move

Black is threatening … ♛xh2 mate here and it appears that there is no defence for White. What winning resource does he have?

HINT
Currently the pawn on g3 is pinned and cannot therefore capture the black queen. How can White change that?

Solution to Puzzle 46

Black draws by 1 … ♖xh3! (threatening 2 … ♛h1 mate) 2 ♛f1 ♖g3+ 3 ♔f2 ♖xf3+ 4 ♔xf3 ♛xf1+ 5 ♔e4 b3 6 axb3 f5+! 7 gxf5 ♛e1+ and White will not be able to escape the checks effectively. 2 ♔xh3? was played in the game but this allowed 2 … ♛h1+ 3 ♛h2 ♛xf3+ 4 ♔xh4 ♗e7+ 5 g5 ♗xg5+! 6 ♔xg5 f6+ 7 ♔h4 g5 mate (diagram).

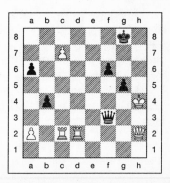

49

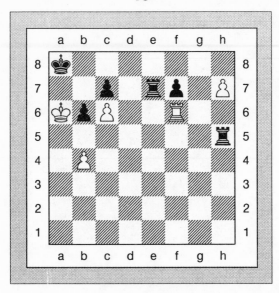

White to move

White is a rook down here and Black is threatening to capture the h7 pawn; is it time for White to resign or is there a resource?

HINT
When all seems lost look for a possible stalemate resource

Solution to Puzzle 47

Black wins material by 1 ... ♗c3+ 2 bxc3 exd6 (diagram). Now his king can escape to g7 and he is the exchange up. The discovered checks now lead nowhere. 1 ... ♕xb5 2 ♕xb5+ ♖xb5 3 ♗c6+ also leads to mate.

50

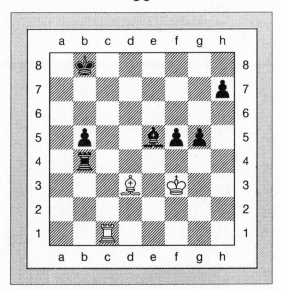

White to move

White is four pawns down here and many players would resign. How can White achieve an unlikely draw?

HINT
Bishops of opposite colours often provide surprising resources

---

Solution to Puzzle 48

White can break the pin by 1 ♘xf3! exf3 2 ♕g7+! ♖xg7 3 ♖e8+ ♖g8 4 ♖xg8+ ♔xg8 5 gxh4 (diagram) and White is two pawns up.

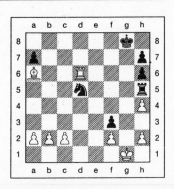

Pawn Endings

51

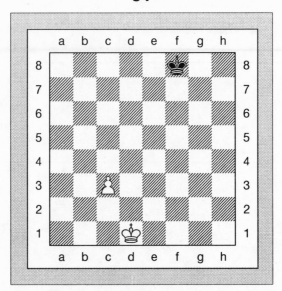

White to move

This shows the basic principles of king and pawn against king rather well. How does White win?

HINT
If Black can get to the square in front of White's pawn, he will draw; how do we stop him?

Solution to Puzzle 49

White drew cleverly by 1 ♖h6! ♖xh6 2 h8=♕+ ♖xh8 3 b5 (diagram). White has no legal moves and will be stalemated after Black's reply, except for 3 ... ♖d7 4 cxd7 c6? 5 bxc6 when it is White who wins!

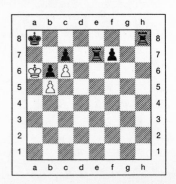

52

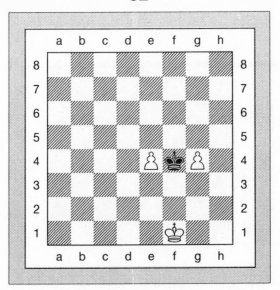

White to move

After solving Position 51, you should have no difficulty finding White's winning move here.

HINT
You need to have a winning plan whichever pawn Black captures next move

---

Solution to Puzzle 50

White draws by 1 ♖c5 g4+ 2 ♔g2 ♖b2+ 3 ♔f1 and now Black has to move his bishop, so 3 … ♗d4 4 ♖xb5+ ♖xb5 5 ♗xb5 ♔c7 6 ♗d3 f4 7 ♗f5! h5 8 ♗g6 h4 9 ♗f5 (diagram) with a complete blockade and a drawn position.

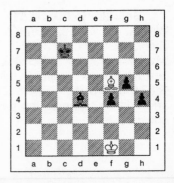

53

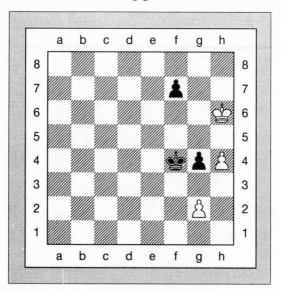

Black to move

White has a passed pawn here while Black does not, so Black has to tread carefully. How does Black save the game?

HINT
It does not look like Black can stop White's pawn, but he does have a simple resource

---

Solution to Puzzle 51

White wins by 1 ♔c2 ♔e7 2 ♔b3 ♔d6 3 ♔b4 (and not 3 ♔c4 ♔c6 which is a draw) 3 … ♔c6 4 ♔c4 and White wins (diagram). If 4 … ♔d6 5 ♔b5 or 4 … ♔b6 5 ♔d5 and White shepherds the pawn onwards.

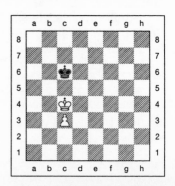

54

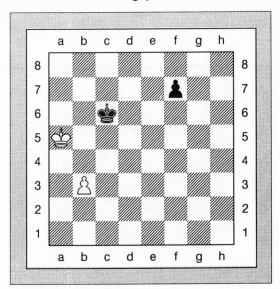

Black to move

A strong Grandmaster failed to find the winning move for Black here; can you do better?

> **HINT**
> **Black needs to combine the threat of advancing his pawn with being able to stop White's pawn**

Solution to Puzzle 52

White wins by 1 ♔f2 with the two symmetrical variations 1 ... ♔xe4 2 ♔g3 ♔e5 3 ♔h4 ♔f6 4 ♔h5 ♔g7 5 ♔g5 and 1 ... ♔xg4 2 ♔e3 ♔g5 3 ♔d4 ♔f6 4 ♔d5 ♔e7 5 ♔e5 (diagram).

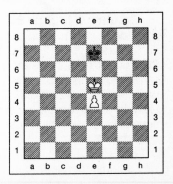

55

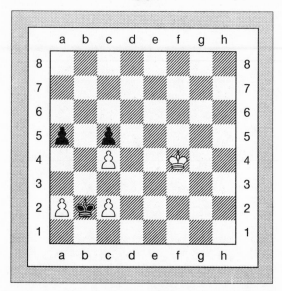

White to move

An International Master resigned here thinking that Black would take the a-pawn and queen his own. How could he have drawn?

HINT
Remember that a pawn on the seventh rank on certain files can draw against a queen

---

Solution to Puzzle 53

Black draws by 1 ... ♔g3 (1 ... g3 also draws) 2 ♔g5 (2 h5 f5 is also a draw as both sides queen) 2 ... f6+! 3 ♔xf6 (3 ♔h5 f5 5 ♔g5 f4 draws easily too) 3 ... ♔xh4 (diagram) with a simple draw. In the game Black played 1 ... f6? which lost after 2 ♔g6 ♔g3 3 h5 ♔xg2 4 h6 g3 5 h7 ♔f1 6 h8=♕ g2 7 ♕xf6+. The queen wins against the pawn here.

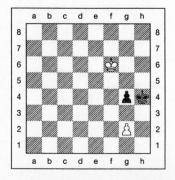

56

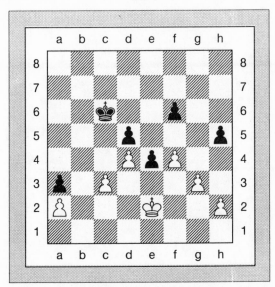

White to move

White has an extra pawn here but care is needed as the backward pawn on c3 is not of much use. How does White win?

HINT
White needs to prepare a breakthrough
on both sides of the board

Solution to Puzzle 54

Black wins by 1 ... ♔d5 (and not 1 ... f5? as played in the game when 3 ♔b4! draws by stopping Black's pawn) 2 b4 f5 3 b5 ♔c6 4 ♔a6 f3 6 b7 f2 7 b8=♕ f1=♕+ (Black queens second but still wins) 8 ♔a5 (or 8 ♔a7 ♕a1 mate) 8 ... ♕a1+ (diagram) and wins the queen next move by a skewer.

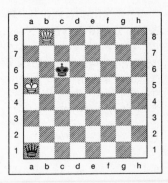

57

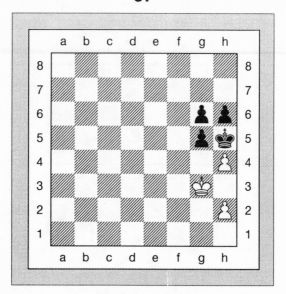

White to move

White is a pawn down here, and yet he had a surprising way to win.
Sometime tactics do occur in king and pawn endings!

HINT
**The black king is boxed in at the edge of the board;
does that suggest a way of winning?**

Solution to Puzzle 55

White could have drawn by 1
♔e4 ♔xa2 2 ♔d5 a4 3 ♔xc5 a3
4 ♔d6 ♔b2 5 c5 a2 6 c6 a1=♕
7 c7 (diagram) and Black cannot
win, despite the presence of
White's pawn on c2, e.g. 7 ...
♕a8 8 ♔d7 ♕d5+ 9 ♔c8 ♔a3
10 c4 with a draw.

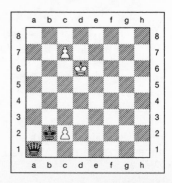

58

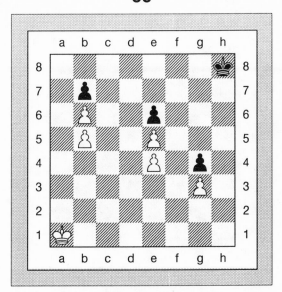

White to move

A blocked position here, but if White can capture a black pawn he will win easily. But where does he move the king?

HINT

When White plays ♔c5, Black has to reply ... ♔e7
and when White moves ♔f4, Black needs to reply ... ♔h5

Solution to Puzzle 56

White wins by 1 f5! (otherwise Black will play ... f5 and White will be unable to break through) 1 ... ♔b5 2 h3! (2 h4 ♔c4 3 g4 hxg4 4 h5 g3 5 h6 g2 6 ♔f2 e3+ 7 ♔xg2 ♔xc3 draws) 2 ... ♔c6 (2 ... ♔c4 3 g4 wins, so the king is forced back) 3 h4! (now 3 g4 hxg4 4 hxg4 ♔d6 5 ♔e3 ♔c6 6 c4 dxc4 7 ♔xe4 ♔d6 draws) 3 ... ♔b5 4 g4 (diagram) and White wins by a tempo.

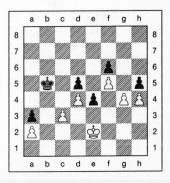

59

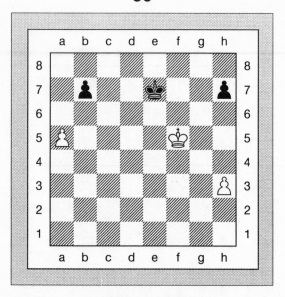

White to move

White has the better placed king here, but it seems hard to achieve anything. A tough problem; how does White win?

HINT
White needs to threaten to head for either pawn, but to be wary of Black's counter-attack on the other one

---

Solution to Puzzle 57
White surprisingly mates in four moves by 1 h3 gxh4+ (1 ... g4 2 hxg4 mate) 2 ♔f4 g5+ 3 ♔f5 g4 4 hxg4 mate (diagram).

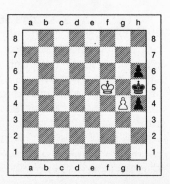

60

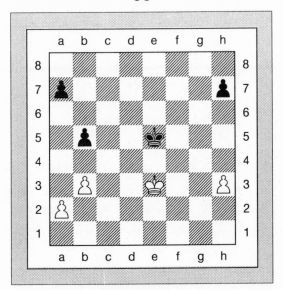

White to move

Black's king is threatening to penetrate on both sides of the board here; how does White create some counterplay?

HINT
White needs to get an advanced pawn so that if Black goes one way he can go the other.

Solution to Puzzle 58

White wins by 1 ♔a2, approaching the centre on corresponding squares, as in the diagram. if 1 ... ♔g7 2 ♔b3 ♔f7 3 ♔b4 ♔f8 4 ♔c4 ♔f7 5 ♔d4 and wins as whichever way Black goes, White goes the other. White must not allow Black to reply by moving his king to a square numbered the same as the one on which White's king stands.

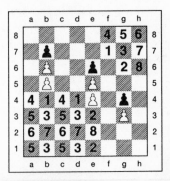

Magical Endgames

61

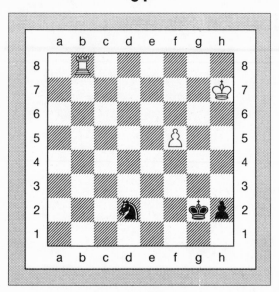

White to move

White seems to have great difficulty stopping the black pawn here, but he does have a resource. How does White draw?

HINT
A bishop's pawn on the seventh sometimes draws against a queen. Does that suggest anything?

Solution to Puzzle 59

White wins by 1 ♔g5 ♔f7 (1 ... ♔d6 2 ♔h6 wins as in the main line) 2 ♔h6 ♔g8 3 h4 ♔h8 4 ♔h5 ♔g8 5 ♔g4! ♔f8 6 ♔f4 ♔e8 7 ♔g5! (doubling back) 7 ... ♔f7 8 ♔f5 ♔e7 9 ♔e5 ♔d7 10 ♔f6 ♔c6 11 ♔g7 ♔b5 12 ♔xh7 ♔xa5 13 ♔g7 b5 14 h5 b4 15 h6 b3 16 h7 b2 17 h8=♕ b1=♕ 18 ♕a8+ (diagram) winning the queen.

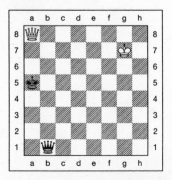

62

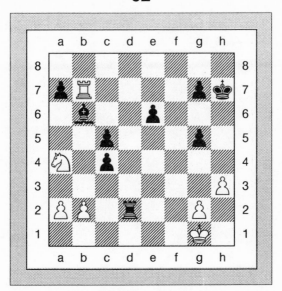

Black to move

This is a famous combination in which the seemingly useless black pawns perform miracles. How does Black win?

> **HINT**
> **A knight can sometimes be very weak at stopping passed pawns. Does that suggest anything?**

Solution to Puzzle 60

The correct method is 1 a4! b4 (if 1 … bxa4 2 bxa4 Black cannot win) 2 a5 h5 (2 … h6 3 h4 draws) 3 ⭐d3! (3 a6 h4 and 3 h4 a6 both win for Black) 3 … ⭐d5 4 h4! (4 ⭐e3 h4 5 ⭐d3 a6 wins) 4 … a6 5 ⭐e3 ⭐e5 6 ⭐d3 ⭐f4 7 ⭐c4 ⭐g4 8 ⭐xb4 ⭐xh4 9 ⭐c5 ⭐g4 10 b4 h4 11 b5 h3 12 b6 draws (diagram). Both sides queen.

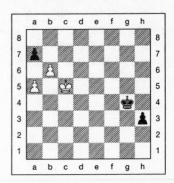

63

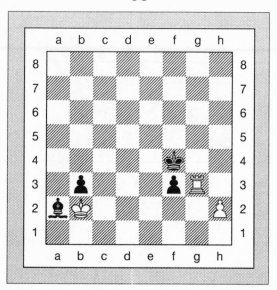

Black to move

It looks like Black has to be careful here but he has a surprising idea which wins. What is it?

HINT
If Black plays 1 ... f2 White will play 2 ♖g8 and win a promoted queen by a skewer. Or will he?

Solution to Puzzle 61

White draws by 1 ♖b1! (and not 1 f6 h1=♕+ 2 ♔g8 ♘e4 winning) 1 ...♘xb1 2 f6 (not 2 ♔g8 ♘c3 3 f6 ♘d5 winning) 2 ... h1=♕+ 3 ♔g8 (diagram) and remarkably Black cannot win. White will play f7 next move.

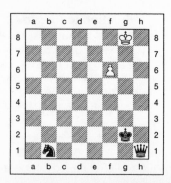

64

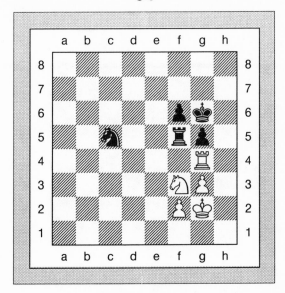

White to move

Material is equal here and the game looks to be heading for a draw, but White has a surprisingly quick win. What is it?

HINT
The fork with 1 ♘h4+ looks promising, but 1 ... ♔h5 counter-attacks the white rook. What then?

Solution to Puzzle 62

Black won by 1 ... ♖xb2 2 ♘xb2 c3 3 ♖xb6 (intending to meet 3 ... axb6 with 4 ♘d3 and 5 ♘c1, but ...) 3 ... c4! 4 ♖b4! a5!! and incredibly one of the black pawns must promote and Black wins (diagram).

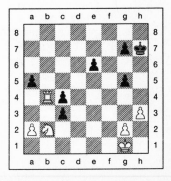

65

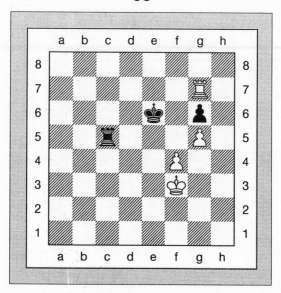

Black to move

Black seems to be in deep trouble here as there is no way to defend the pawn on g6. How does Black achieve a draw?

HINT
When all seems lost look for a possible stalemate resource

Solution to Puzzle 63
Black wins by the surprising 1 ... f2 2 ♖g8 ♗b1! (diagram). Now if White plays 2 ♔xb1, the pawn promotes *with check*, while 2 ♖f8+ is met by 2 ... ♗f5 and the black pawn promotes.

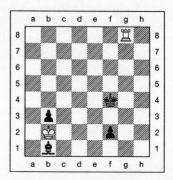

66

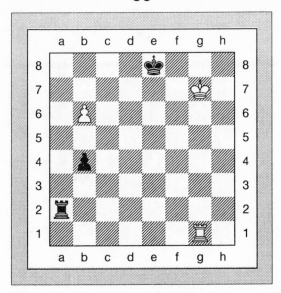

White to move

Only one pawn each here; how does White use his further advanced pawn to force a win?

HINT
It seems that advancing the pawn with 1 b7
just loses it to the pin 1 ... ☖a7, but is that so?

Solution to Puzzle 64
After 1 ♘h4+ ♚h5 2 ♘xf5 ♚xg4, White has the surprising 3 ♘g7 and Black cannot prevent f3 mate (diagram).

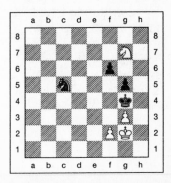

67

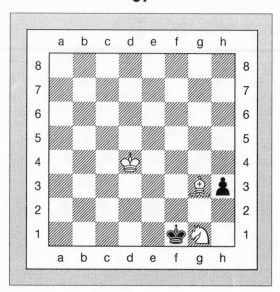

White to move

Bishop and knight will win against a king, but here White seems to have a problem keeping both pieces. How does he win?

HINT
You do have to lose a piece, so you have to use the black pawn to help you checkmate with the other one!

Solution to Puzzle 65

Black draws after 1 … ♖c6! 2 ♖xg6+ (2 ♔e4 ♖c4+ 3 ♔e3 ♔f5 is drawing for Black; 2 ♔g4 ♔d5 3 ♖f7 ♖a6 4 ♖f6 ♖xf6 5 gxf6 ♔e6 is also a draw.) 2 … ♔f5 3 ♖xc6 stalemate (diagram).

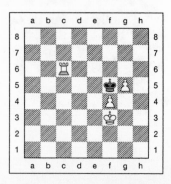

68

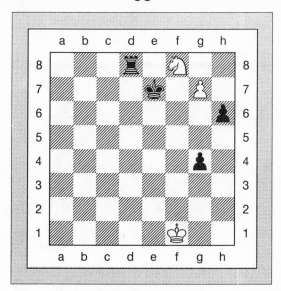

White to move

White seems to have problems in the above position, but he has a clever way to draw. What is it?

HINT
Promoting to a queen allows 1 ... ♖xf8+ with a winning king and pawn ending. Is there anything else?

Solution to Puzzle 66

White has a little tactical trick to win the black rook after 1 b7 ♖a7 2 ♖e1+ ♔d8 3 ♖e7! (diagram). Now the pin is broken and 3 ... ♔xe7 4 b8=♕ is a technical but difficult win with queen against rook.

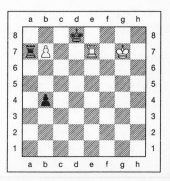

69

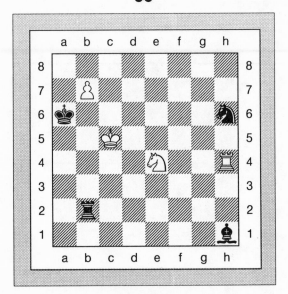

White to move

White is a piece down here but can recover the material easily. However the task is for White to win. How?

HINT
Black is hemmed in at the edge of the board; keeping him there is the most important factor

---

Solution to Puzzle 67

White must imprison the black king with 1 ♗h2! ♔g2 2 ♔e3 ♔xh2 3 ♔f2 ♔h1 4 ♘e2 ♔h2 5 ♘d4 ♔h1 6 ♘f5 ♔h2 7 ♘e3 ♔h1 8 ♘f1 h2 9 ♘g3 mate (diagram).

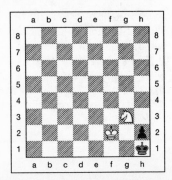

70

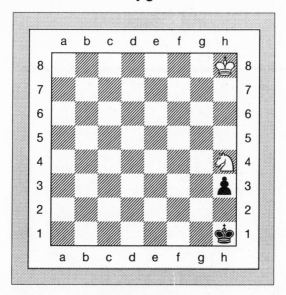

White to move

All White needs to do here is to give up the knight for the pawn; but that is easier said than done; how does White draw?

HINT
Black is going to play ... ♔g1, ... ♔f2 and only then ... h2. How does White meet the threat?

Solution to Puzzle 68
White can draw by 1 g8=♘+ ♔xf8 2 ♘xh6 ♖d4 3 ♔g2 and Black cannot save his g-pawn (diagram). 3 ... ♔g7 allows a fork on f5. White reaches a drawn position with king and knight v king and rook.

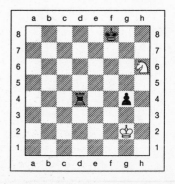

Endgame Studies

71

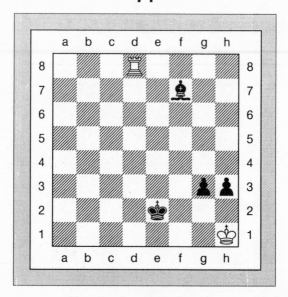

White to move and draw

The black pawns look menacing in the above position but White can stop them with a clever resource.

HINT
White's rook cannot leave the d-file because of 1 … ♗d5+ but how does he stop Black getting his bishop to f3?

Solution to Puzzle 69

White wins by giving up his passed pawn with 1 b8=♕! (1 ♘d6 ♖c2+ draws, as does 1 ♖h2 ♖b5+) 1 … ♖xb8 2 ♘d6 (threatening ♖a4 mate) 2 … ♗c6! 3 ♖h3! (renewing the threat; 3 ♖h2? ♗d5! draws) 3 … ♗a4! 4 ♖a3 ♔a5 5 ♘c4+ ♔a6 6 ♖xa4+ ♔b7 7 ♘d6+ ♔c7 8 ♖a7+ ♔d8 9 ♔c6 (diagram) and Black can only delay mate.

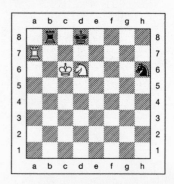

72

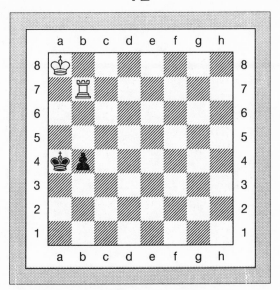

White to move and win

White needs to play accurately to win the black pawn;
how do the king and rook combine to do so?

HINT
**White will have to bring his king across the b-file;
at what point does he do that?**

Solution to Puzzle 70
The only move to draw is 1 ♘g6!
♔g1 (1 ... h2 2 ♘h4! draws as
2 ... ♔g1 is forced and then 3
♘f3+ as in the game) 2 ♘e5 h2
(2 ... ♔f2 3 ♘g4+ draws) 3 ♘f3+
(diagram) drawing.

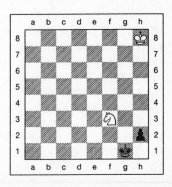

73

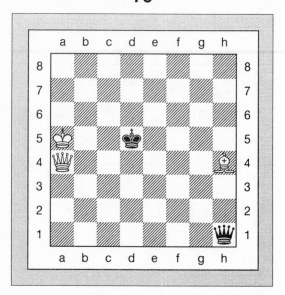

White to move and win

The white forces look poorly co-ordinated in the diagram, but a series of checks forces the win of the black queen. How?

HINT
The skewer on the long diagonal is White's main ally here; how does White force the black king onto it?

Solution to Puzzle 71

White draws by the clever defence 1 ♖d4 ♗h5 2 ♖h4 ♔f2 (2 ...♗f3+ 3 ♔g1 is a draw as Black is controlling h2) 3 ♖g4! with a spectacular draw (diagram). Now 3 ... h2 4 ♖f4+ draws and 3 ...g2+ 4 ♔h2 is also a draw. 2 ♖e4+ ♔f2 3 ♖g4! is an alternative way to reach the same position.

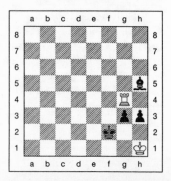

74

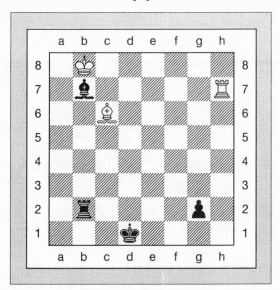

White to move and draw

Black has an extra pawn here and is also threatening some unpleasant discovered checks. How does White save the game?

HINT
White needs to give up the bishop for the pawn
without allowing … ♗e4+ winning the rook

Solution to Puzzle 72

The winning technique is 1 ♔a7 b3 2 ♔a6! (not 2 ♔b6 ♔b4 which fends off the black king and draws) 2 … ♔a3 3 ♔b5 b2 4 ♔c4 ♔a2 5 ♖a8+ ♔b1 6 ♔b3 ♔c1 7 ♖c8+ (diagram) winning the pawn.

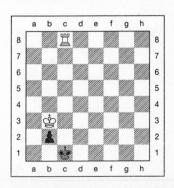

75

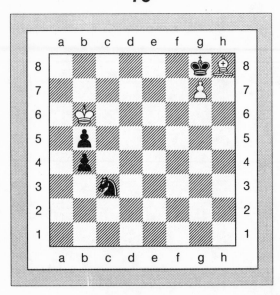

White to move

It looks impossible for White to draw here as a black pawn must queen. Which surprising resource comes to White's rescue?

HINT
The only chance for White here is stalemate.
Where does he want his king when Black promotes?

Solution to Puzzle 73

White wins 1 ♕d7+ ♔c4 (1 ... ♔e5 2 ♕g7+ ♔e6 3 ♕e7+ ♔f5 4 ♕f6+ ♔g4 5 ♕g5+ wins the queen) 2 ♕b5+ ♔d4 3 ♗f2+ ♔c3 4 ♗e1+ ♔d4 5 ♕b2+ ♔c5 6 ♕b6+ ♔c4 7 ♕b4+ ♔d3 8 ♕c3+ ♔e2 9 ♕d2+ mating or winning the queen (diagram). You may enjoy checking that Black loses his queen in all the sidelines as well.

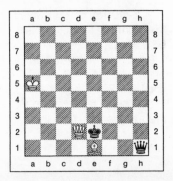

76

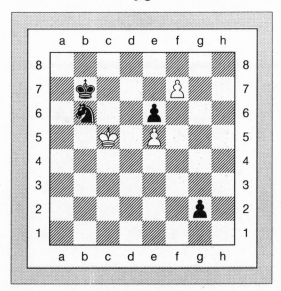

White to move

Black is a piece up here, but knights are usually poor at stopping passed pawns. How does White achieve a draw?

HINT
Promoting the pawn to a queen allows a fork;
so what should White play?

Solution to Puzzle 74

White needs to move the rook first, so 1 ♖d7+ ♚c1 2 ♗xg2, but 2 ... ♗c6+ seems to win on material. However 3 ♖b7! ♖xb7+ 4 ♚a8! is a surprising draw a rook down (diagram). You try to win for Black!

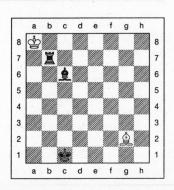

77

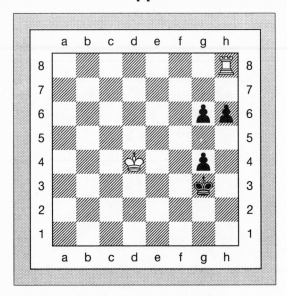

White to move and win

The struggle between a rook and passed pawns is always interesting. How does White round them up here?

HINT
1 ♖xh6 is too slow after 1 ... ♚f2 followed by 2 ... g3.
So 1 ♚e3 looks right; what happens after 1 ... h5?

Solution to Puzzle 75

White draws by 1 ♚c5 (not 1 ♚a5 ♞d5 winning) 1 ... b3 (1 ... ♞d5 2 ♚d4 b3 3 ♚d3 stops the pawns and draws) 2 ♚b4 b2 3 ♚a3 ♞d1 (promoting to queen or rook is stalemate; promoting to a bishop or knight only draws as the reader can establish; 3 ... ♞a4 leads to the same finish.) 4 ♚a2 b4 5 ♚b1 b3 stalemate (diagram).

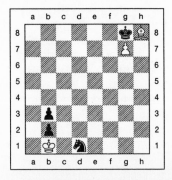

78

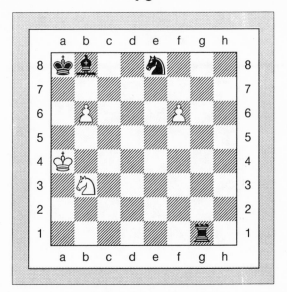

White to move and win

The white pawns are very threatening in this position; finding Black's resources is the main task.

HINT
After the obvious 1 f7 White seems to promote; however Black has a stalemate defence.

Solution to Puzzle 76

White draws by 1 ♔d6! Now 1 ... g1=♕ 2 f8=♕ ♕c5+ sems to win after 3 ♔xc5 ♘d7+ and 4 ... ♘xf8. However White plays 3 ♔xe6! ♕xf8 stalemate. The only try to avoid this is 1 ... g1=♗! and if 2 f8=♕ ♗c5+ really does win, but 2 f8=♘! is a draw (diagram). Black cannot save his pawn.

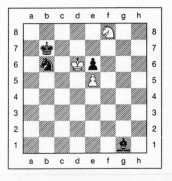

79

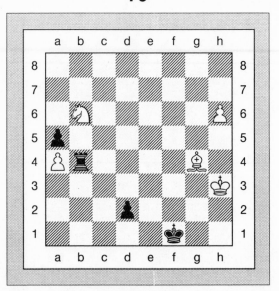

White to move

White's knight is attacked here and Black is threatening … ♖xg4
followed by queening his pawn. How does White draw?

> ### HINT
> **White has to get somewhere with his pawn on h6,
> but 1 h7 ♖xg4 2 h8=♕ d1=♕ is hopeless for White**

Solution to Puzzle 77

After 1 ♔e3 h5 White wins with
2 ♔e2 (2 ♖h6 h4 3 ♔e2 h3 4
♔f1 ♔h2 5 ♖xg6 g3 6 ♖g8 g2+
draws) 2 … ♔g2 3 ♖h7! waiting
(and not 3 ♖h6? g3 which is
zugzwang) 3 … g3 4 ♖h6! ♔h2
(4 … ♔g1 5 ♔h3 wins) 5 ♖xg6
h4 (5 … ♔g2 6 ♖h6) 6 ♔f3 ♔g1
7 ♖g4 (diagram) winning both
pawns.

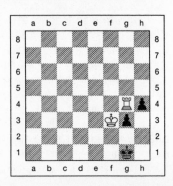

80

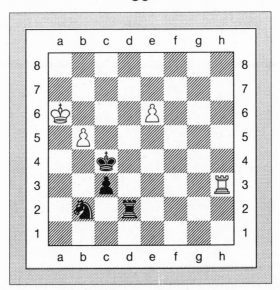

White to move

Black's pawn is on the brink of queening here; how does White get enough counterplay with his own pawns to draw?

HINT
After 1 b6 ♘a4 White cannot play 2 b7 because of the fork on c5. Does that suggest anything?

Solution to Puzzle 78
After 1 f7 ♖g4+ 2 ♔a5 ♖g5+ the only way to make progress is 3 ♔a6. But now 3 ... ♘c7+ 4 bxc7 ♖g8. If White promotes to a rook or queen it is stalemate, but 5 fxg8=♗! wins after 5 ... ♗xc7 6 ♘d4 (threatening ♘c6 and a later mate on b7 with the bishop) 6 ... ♔b8 7 ♘c6+ ♔c8 8 ♗e6 mate (diagram). An ideal mate.

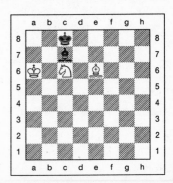

Problems

81

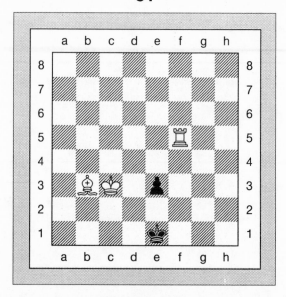

White to move

It is easy enough for White to win here, but how can he force mate in three moves?

HINT
You need to be able to cope with the advance of Black's pawn; how do you do that?

Solution to Puzzle 79

White has to give up the knight first with 1 ♘c4! (1 ♘d5 ♖xg4 2 h7 ♔g1! 3 ♘e3 ♖e4 wins for Black) 1 ... ♖xc4 2 h7 ♖xg4 3 h8=♕ d1=♕ 4 ♕f6+ ♔g1 and White looks lost. However 5 ♕c3! surprisingly draws, with what is known as a position of mutual *zugzwang* (diagram). If Black tries to keep his rook White can give up his queen to force stalemate.

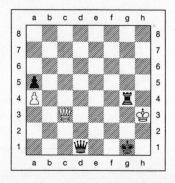

82

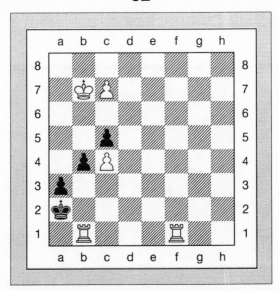

White to move

The Black king is cornered here but it is still quite tricky for White fo force mate in four moves. Can you find it?

HINT
Black is going to play ... b3 and ... b2 and if his king is stopped from going to b3 it is stalemate; or is it?

Solution to Puzzle 80

White has to give up his rook after 1 b6 ♘a4 (1 ... ♖e2 2 ♖xc3+ ♔xc3 3 b7 draws) 2 ♖h4+ ♔b3 3 ♖xa4 ♔xa4 4 b7 ♖d8 5 ♔a7 c2 6 e7 ♖e8 7 b8=♕ ♖xe7+ 8 ♔a8 c1=♕ and Black seems to win. However 9 ♕f4+! ♕xf4 is stalemate (diagram).

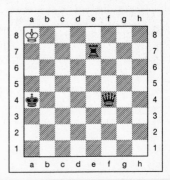

83

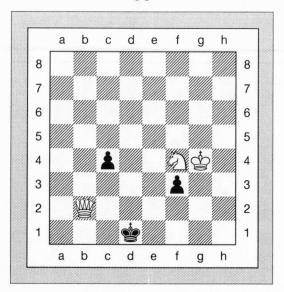

White to move

Queen and knight co-ordinate well, but it is surprisingly difficult for White to mate in three moves. Cany you solve it?

HINT
You need to cope with either pawn advance here
and to look out for stalemate

Solution to Puzzle 81

White mates in three by 1 ♗f7! and now:

a) 1 ...♔d1 2 ♖f1+ and 3 ♗c4 mate;

b) 1 ... ♔e2 2 ♗c4+ and 3 ♖f1 mate;

c) 1 ... e2 2 ♗h5 ♔d1 3 ♖f1 mate (diagram).

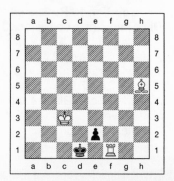

84

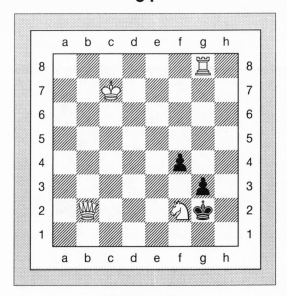

White to move

Black seems to have a lot of escape squares here, but White can still mate in three moves. How?

HINT
The white knight is in the way a little; that suggests moving it to a useful square

---

Solution to Puzzle 82
White needs to underpromote the pawn with 1 c8=♗! b3 2 ♗g4 b2 3 ♗d1 ♔xb1 4 ♗b3 mate (diagram). The bishop is needed to allow the rook on b1 to be captured!

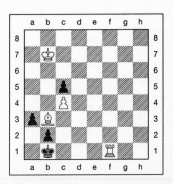

85

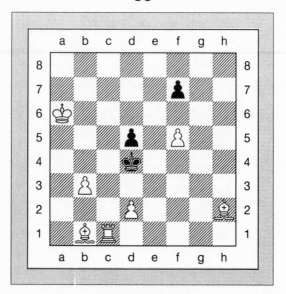

White to move

Black is short of flight squares here; but White has to mate in three moves.

> **HINT**
> **Black has only one legal move so you need to look out for stalemate**

Solution to Puzzle 83

The only way to mate in three is to offer the knight with 1 ♘d3; now:

a) 1 ... cxd3 2 ♔xf3 and mate next move;

b) 1 ...c3 2 ♕f2 and mate next move;

c) 1 ...f2 2 ♕c1+ ♔e2 3 ♘f4 mate (diagram).

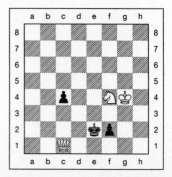

86

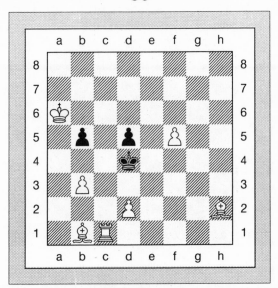

White to move

This is the twin position of the one opposite. Again White has to mate in three moves.

HINT
Again Black has stalemate possibilities;
they key is similar to number 85 but different!

Solution to Puzzle 84

White mates in three by 1 ♘g4+; now:
a) 1... ♔f1 or 1 ... ♔g1 2 ♖a8 and mate next move on a1;
b) 1... ♔f3 2 ♕c2 g2 3 ♕d3 mate;
c) 1... ♔h3 2 ♘h2 and mate next move with ♕h8 or ♖h8;
d) 1... ♔h1 2 ♕h2+ gxh2 3 ♘f2 mate (diagram).

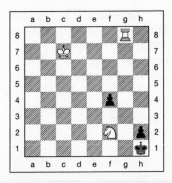

87

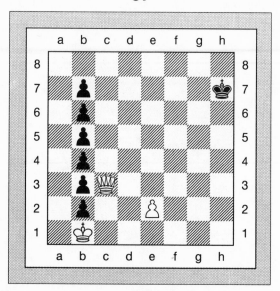

White to move

An unusual position and a tricky problem. White is to play and force Black to deliver checkmate in 21 moves.

> **HINT**
> **Selfmates are usually easier than they appear.**
> **Here all Black's moves are forced.**

Solution to Puzzle 85

White needs to block the diagonal quickly and only 1 ♗b8 achieves this; then 1 ... f6 2 ♖c7 ♔e5 3 ♖c4 mate (diagram).

The attempt 1 ♖c8 f6 2 ♗c7 fails because Black has a flight square on b4.

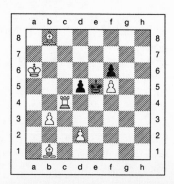

88

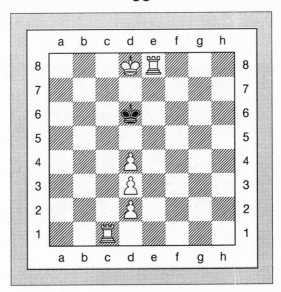

White to move

Two white rooks should mate fairly quickly, but here the task is for White to mate in four moves.

> **HINT**
> Black can not be allowed to escape from the
> d-file; but how do we mate him there?

Solution to Puzzle 86

This time White needs to block the c-file with 1 ♖c8 b4 2 ♗c7 ♔c5 3 ♗e5 mate (diagram).

This time 1 ♗c7 b4 2 ♖c7 fails because Black has a flight square on f6. Together these "twins" illustrate the so-called Indian theme, where the key in one is the try in the other, and vice versa.

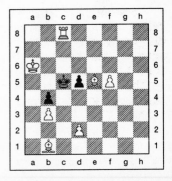

89

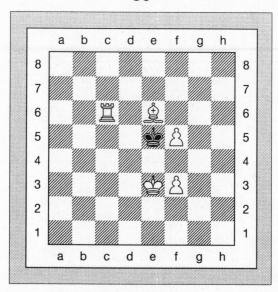

White to move

A problem with a difference. White has to deliver checkmate in five moves, but with the pawn on f3!

HINT
Black's king must not be allowed to stray too far from its current square

---

Solution to Puzzle 87
White has to drive the black king around to a3 by 1 ♕f6 ♚g8 2 e4 ♚h7 3 e5 ♚g8 4 e6 ♚h7 5 e7 ♚g8 6 e8=♘ ♚h7 7 ♘d6 ♚g8 8 ♘f5 ♚h7 9 ♕h6+ ♚g8 10 ♕h5 ♚f8 11 ♕h7 ♚e8 12 ♕g7 ♚d8 13 ♕e7+ ♚c8 14 ♘d6+ ♚b8 15 ♕d8+ ♚a7 16 ♕c8 ♚a6 17 ♕xb7+ ♚a5 18 ♘e4 ♚a4 19 ♕xb6 ♚a3 20 ♘c3 bxc3 21 ♕xb5 c2 mate (diagram).

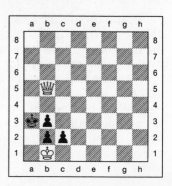

90

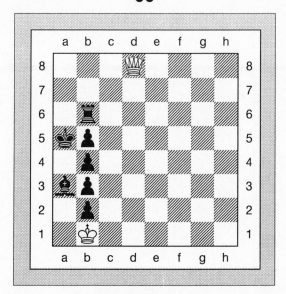

White to move

A tough problem in which White can force mate in ten moves. How?

HINT
If Black were on move here he would have to play ... ♚a6 allowing ♕a8 mate. Can we engineer that?

Solution to Puzzle 88
White needs to defend the d3 pawn as we shall see, so 1 ♖c3 ♚d5 2 ♚e7 ♚xd4 3 ♚f6 ♚d5 4 ♖d8 mate (see diagram).

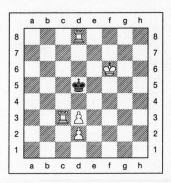

Unusual Positions

91

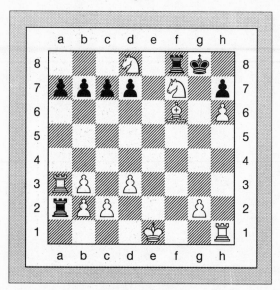

White to move

This is known as a "retro" problem, where some backward thinking is needed. All we are asking you here is can White castle?

> **HINT**
> This is a logic problem; firstly you have to work out
> Black's last move which should not take you long

Solution to Puzzle 89
White mates in five moves using the pawn on f3 by 1 ♗c8 ♔d5 2 ♗b7 ♔e5 3 ♖g6 ♔xf5 4 ♗e4+ ♔e5 5 f4 mate (diagram).

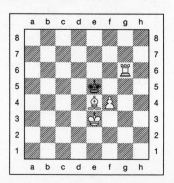

92

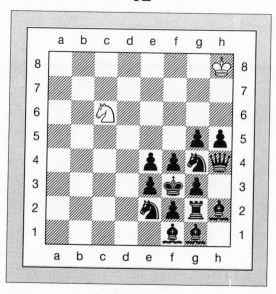

White to move

Black's pieces are completely boxed in; how does White mate in 12 moves?

HINT
Clearly Black can only shuffle his queen to and fro; in what way can the white king help?

Solution to Puzzle 90

White mates by a series of neat manoeuvres: 1 ♕a8+ ♖a6 2 ♕b8 ♖a8 (2 ... ♔a4 3 ♕c7 mates in 7) 3 ♕b7 ♖a6 4 ♕c7+ ♔a4 (if 4... ♖b6 5 ♕d8 gets the initial position with Black to move) 5 ♕d8 ♖a7 (5 ... ♖a5 6 ♕b8 is the same) 6 ♕b8 ♖a6 (6 ... ♖a5 7 ♕b7 mates in 8) 7 ♕c7 ♖a8 8 ♕b6 ♖a5 9 ♕b7 (diagram) and mate next move.

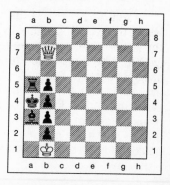

9/28/02

93

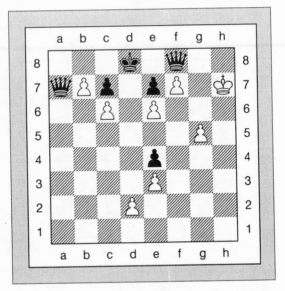

White to move

Black is two queens up in the diagram but they are both somewhat constrained. How does White exploit this?

HINT
Black intends to go 1.. ♛b6 and 2... ♛b2.
How do we stop this?

Solution to Puzzle 91

No, White cannot castle and the logic is interesting. Firstly Black's last move must also have been to castle. The rook on a2 must therefore be a promoted rook, because the rook on a8 could not have escaped. If it promoted on d1 or f1, White would have to have moved his king. If it promoted on g1 it could not have got out without White moving his king or rook. Finally if it promoted on a1, then the black e-pawn must have made four captures on d6, c5, b4 and a3, but one of the four missing pieces is the white-squared bishop which could not have been captured on a black square. Therefore White must have moved his king or rook at some point in the game.

94

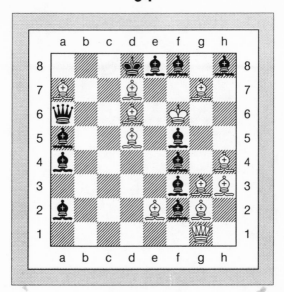

White to move

A strange but legal position which you will have problems setting up unless you have five chess sets. White to mate in four moves.

HINT
In a sense White plays the same move every time ... and so does Black

---

Solution to Puzzle 92

White must choose the king route carefully to give the move to Black. So 1 ♔g7 ♕h3 2 ♔f8 ♕h4 3 ♔e7 ♕h3 4 ♔d6 ♕h4 5 ♔e6 ♕h3 6 ♔e7 ♕h4 7 ♔f8 ♕h3 8 ♔g7 ♕h4 9 ♔g6 ♕h3 10 ♔xg5 ♕h4+ 11 ♔xh4 (diagram) and mate next move.

95

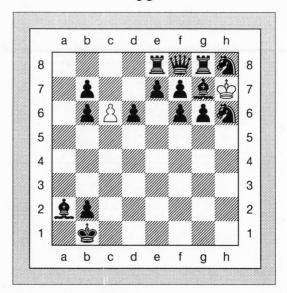

White to move

White has a solitary pawn against the entire black army here, but he can force a draw. How?

> **HINT**
> After 1 c7 g5 Black is threatening to move his king and mate White by promoting on b1

Solution to Puzzle 93

White wins by 1 d4! exd3 (Black must capture because the diagonal is now blocked; 1 ... ♛b6 2 g6 ♛b1 3 b8=♛+! ♛xb8 4 g7 wins) 2 g6 d2 3 g7 ♛xg7+ 4 ♔xg7 ♛a1+ 5 ♔g8 ♛g1+ (if Black's d-pawn were immobile Black could force stalemate with 5 ... ♛g7+) 6 ♔f8 ♛b1 7 b8=♛+! ♛xb8 8 ♔g8 (diagram) and mates next move.

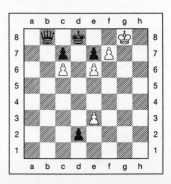

96

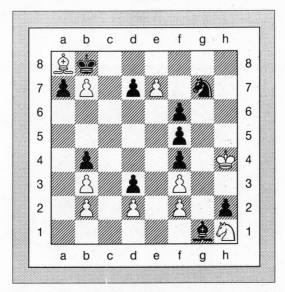

White to move

Not much can move here; but White still has to find a way to break through. How does White improve his position and force a win?

Solution to Puzzle 94

Amusingly each side captures a bishop on each move. 1 ♔xf5+ ♔xd7 2 ♔xf4+ ♔xd6 3 ♔xf3+ ♔xd5 4 ♔xf2 mate (diagram).

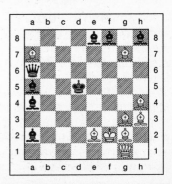

97

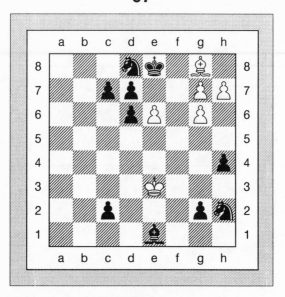

White to move

A strange position in which Black is queening with check on both c1 and g1 and yet White can win. How?

HINT
In view of Black's threats, White needs to win with a series of checks; that should help you

---

Solution to Puzzle 95

White draws by 1 c7 g5 2 c8=♖! (2 c8=♕ loses to 2 ... ♔a1 3 ♕c1+ b1=♕+ forcing mate) 2 ... ♔a1 3 ♖c2! ♗c4 (the best chance; if Black promotes to a queen it is stalemate) 4 ♖c1+ ♔a2 5 ♖a1+ (diagram) and the white rook can chase the black king around the board and force a draw by stalemate!

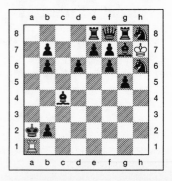

98

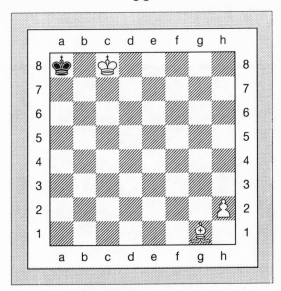

Someone to move

You arrive at the end of this game to see that Black has resigned. But what were White's and Black's last moves?

HINT
If Black moved his king from a7, how did White give check with the bishop on g1?

Solution to Puzzle 96

White needs to triangulate in the bottom left corner while Black shuffles his knight to and fro. White plays ♔h3-g2-f1-e1-d1-c1-b1-a2-a1-b1-c1-d1-e1-f1-g2-h3-h4 reaching the starting position with Black to move. Black has to move a pawn and White repeats the procedure until Black runs out of pawn moves eventually reaching the diagram opposite.

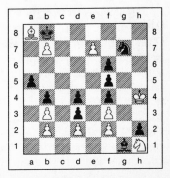

99

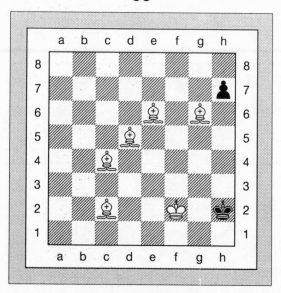

White to move

Normally even two bishops are enough to win against a pawn but here all five are on the same colour squares. How does White win?

HINT
The black pawn needs to be forced to h2,
and this involves sacrificing two of the bishops

Solution to Puzzle 97

White wins by 1 ♗f7+ ♔e7 2 g8=♘+ ♔f8 3 e7+ ♔g7 4 e8=♘+ ♔h8 5 g7+ ♔xh7 6 ♘gf6+ ♔h6 7 g8=♘+ ♔g5 8 ♘e4+ ♔f5 (8 ... ♔g4 9 ♘e8f6+ ♔h3 10 ♘g5+ ♔g3 11 ♘fe4+ ♔g4 12 ♘h6 mate) 9 ♘e7+ ♔e5 10 ♘g6+ ♔f5 11 ♘g7+ ♔g4 12 ♘e5+ dxe5 13 ♗h5+ ♔h3 14 ♘g5+ ♔g3 15 ♘f5 mate (diagram)

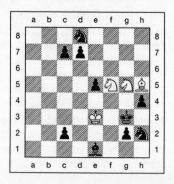

100

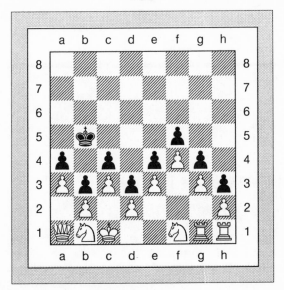

White to move

White has a huge material advantage in this position but it looks extremely difficult for White to breakthrough. Any ideas?

HINT
White needs to arrange his pieces correctly and then play the move ♕a2 in order to capture on b3

Solution to Puzzle 98

Firstly it must be White to move. If Black were to move it would be stalemate and Black could not resign. Black's last move was to capture a knight on a8 with ... ♚xa8. White's previous move was ♘a8 discovered check. This was the position one move ago:

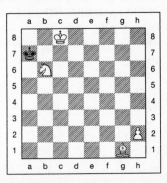

Solution to Puzzle 99

White wins by 1 ♗ge4 h5 2 ♗h1 h4 3 ♗ce4 h3 4 ♔f3! ♔xh1 5 ♔g3+ Kg1 6 ♗h1 h2 7 ♔f3 ♔xh1 8 ♔f2 mate (see diagram). If Black starts with 1 ... h6 White just waits with one of his bishops.

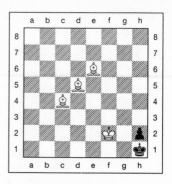

Solution to Puzzle 100

Black shuffles between a6 and b6 while White plays ♔d1, ♔e1, ♔f2, ♖g2, ♔g1, ♖e2, ♖e1, ♖c1, ♔f2, ♖g1, ♖g2, ♔e1, ♖e2, ♔d1, ♖e1, ♖c2, ♔c1, ♕a2 reaching the diagram. Now 18 ... bxa2 is forced but then 19 b4! (not 19 b3 a1=♕ 20 ♖b2 axb3 drawing). If 19 ... b1=♕ 20 ♖b2 wins. If 19 .. axb3 20 ♖xa2 wins. If 19 ... dxc2 20 ♔b2 wins

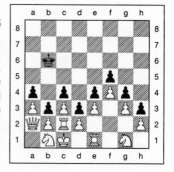

It is interesting that no computer program has ever been able to solve position 100 and Fritz and Hiarcs, two of the strongest machines, do not find 18 ♕a2 when given the position one move before the diagram. There is still a problem in conceptual visualisation with computers. Position 61 also proved beyond any of the current computers, as the idea that the resulting position with a pawn against queen and knight might be drawn is beyond the machine's comprehension.

Sources of Positions

Acknowledgements are due to John Roycroft for tracing some sources

1   Composed position
2   Composed position
3   Position from a simultaneous display by the author
4   Lamford v P.Wells, Rapidplay, Basingstoke 1979
5   Game against Fritz Chess Program
6   Position from a simultaneous display by the author
7   Composed position
8   Composed position
9   Position from a simultaneous display by the author
10   Composed position
11   Composed position
12   Anderssen-Zukertort, Barmen 1869
13   Karpov-Kavalek, Turin 1982
14   Sanakoyev-Zagorovsky, Voronezh 1972
15   Ivanov-Dimitrov, Sofia 1957
16   Abrahams-Winter, London 1946
17   Hemsohn-Heisenrutter, West Germany 1958
18   Pougayevsky-Szilagyi, Moscow 1960
19   W.Cohn-Steinitz, Cologne 1898
20   Wachtel-Musiol, Poland 1953
21   Larsen-Spassky, Linares 1981
22   Zaitsev-Suetin, USSR Ch 1952
23   Utasi-Filguth, Hungary 1986
24   Gipslis-Kostro, Dubna 1976
25   Haik-Fuller, London 1977
26   Forintos-Tomovic, Budapest v Belgrade 1957
27   Zakharov-Litvinov, Minsk 1978
28   Schiffers-Chigorin, Berlin 1897
29   Christoffel-P.Müller, Zurich 1965
30   Stefanov-Andreyev, Bulgaria 1957
31   Alekhine's Defence after 1 e4 ♘f6 2 ♘c3 d5 3 e5 ♘d4 4
      ♘ce2 d4 5 c3 dxc3
32   The Hungarian Defence after 1 e4 e5 2 ♘f3 ♘c6 3 ♗e4
      ♗e7 4 d4 exd4 5 c3 dxc3
33   The Queen's Gambit Declined after 1 d4 d5 2 c4 e6 3 ♘c3 ♘f6 4
      ♗g5 ♘bd7 5 cxd5 exd5

34   The Sicilian Defence, Velimirovic Attack, after 1 e4 c5 2 ♘f3 ♘c6 3
         d4 cxd4 4 ♘xd4 ♘xf6 5 ♘c3 d6 6 ♗c4 e6 7 ♗e3 a6 8 ♕e2 ♕c7
         9 0-0-0 b5 10 ♗d3 ♗b7 11 g4 d5 12 ♗g5 ♘xe4 13 ♘xe4 dxe4 14
         ♗xe4 ♕e5?

35   The English Opening after 1 c4 e5 2 ♘f3 ♘c6 3 ♘f3 f5 4 ♗g5
         ♘f6

36   Analysis of a variation of the wild Traxler Counter Attack in the
         Two Knight's Defence

37   French Defence after 1 e4 e6 2 d4 d5 3 ♘c3 ♗b4 4 ♘e2 dxe4 5
         a3 ♗xc3+ 6 ♘xc3 ♘f6 7 ♗g5! ♘c6 8 ♗b5 0-0 9 ♗xc6 bxc6 10
         ♘xe4 ♕d5 11 ♘xf6+ gxf6 12 ♗xf6 ♕xg2

38   Caro-Kann Defence after 1 e4 c6 2 d4 d5 3 ♘c3 dxe4 4 ♘xe4
         ♘d7 5 ♗c4 ♘gf6 6 ♘g5 e6 7 ♕e2 ♘b6 8 ♗d3 h6 9 ♘5f3 c5 10
         dxc5 ♘bd7 11 c6 bxc6 12 ♘d4 c5?

39   The Latvian Gambit after 1 e4 e5 2 ♘f3 f5 3 ♗c4 fxe4 4 ♘xe5
         ♕g5 6 d4 ♕xg2 7 ♗f7+ ♚d8 8 ♗xg6 ♕xh1+ 9 ♚e7 c6 10 ♘c3
         ♘f6 11 ♕g5! ♗e7 12 ♗f4 ♕xa1 13 ♘f7+ ♚e8 14 ♘xh8+ hxg6 15
         ♕xg6+ ♚d8

40   Slav Defence after 1 d4 d5 2 c4 c6 3 ♘f3 ♗f5 4 ♕b3 ♕b6 5 cxd5
         ♕xb3 6 axb3 ♗xb1?

41   Nemeth-Zsinka, Heilbad Harkany 1987
42   Mathot-Baumgartner, correspondence 1958
43   Puig-Larsson, Leipzig 1960
44   Bernasconi-Weissen, Disentis 1983
45   Bezenaru-S.Szabo, Gemsivar 1956
46   Bouaziz-Miles, Riga Interzonal 1979
47   Krassilnikov-Beckmann, correspondence 1975
48   Onescius-Gama, Rumanian Championship 1955
49   Marshall-Maclure, New York 1923
50   Norwood-Rødgaard, London 1986
51   Y.Averbakh and I.Maizelis, *Pawn Endings* 1974
52   E.Pogosyants 1970
53   Taimanov-Mestel, London 1976
54   Ljubojevic-Browne, Amsterdam 1972
55   Belkadi-Pachman, Munich Olympiad 1958
56   P.A.Lamford, *British Chess Magazine* 1986
57   A.W.Galitsky, *La Stratégie* 1900
60   P.A.Lamford, *British Chess Magazine* 1987
61   P.A.Lamford, 1983
62   Tylkowski-Wojchiechowski, Championship of Poznan 1931
63   Missed win in Borisenko-Myesyenyev, All-Union Tournament of
         Collective Farmworkers 1950
64   Players unknown

65	Variation from Kotov-Pachman, Venice 1950
66	Composer unknown
67	P.A.Lamford 1978, using an ancient position with knight v pawn
68	Players or composer unknown
69	P.A.Lamford, *EG 68* 1982
70	R.Turnbull, *BCM* 1996
71	Pál Benkö, *EG* 1982
72	E.Pogosyants, 1970
73	M.Havel, First Prize, *Shakhmaty* 1926
74	D.Gurgenidze and V.Kalandadze, *64* 1972
75	G A Nadereishvili, First Prize, "Akhalgasrda Komunisti" 1957
76	V.Yakimchik, *Shakmaty v SSSR 1933*
77	J.D.M.Nunn, *Schaakbulletin* 1982
78	D. Gurgenidze, First Prize *The Problemist* 1984-5
79	P.A.Lamford and J.S.Speelman, *British Chess Magazine* 1986
80	P.A.Lamford and V.Nestorescu, *British Chess Magazine* 1986
81	Bata Lörinc, *Bilten* 1962
82	Composer unknown; shown by a Mr Isenburger to B.H.Wood in 1952
83	Pál Benkö, *Chess Life* 1967
84	Sam Loyd, First Special Prize, *Chess Monthly* 1857
85	Edmond Bernard, *Tribune de Genève* 1976
86	Edmond Bernard, *Tribune de Genève* 1976
87	Dr Beresi Gyull, *The Fairy Chess Review* 1955
88	Y.Selavkin, *Chess* 1977
89	J.Kling, 1848
90	G.Jahn, Special Prize, *Die Schwalbe* 1979
91	Lord Dunsany, date unknown
92	Dr K.I.Fabel, 1952
93	P.A.Lamford, version of a study published in *British Chess Magazine* 1986
94	Hugh Courtney, *Chess* 1976
95	A.J.Roycroft, *British Chess Magazine* 1952
96	E.Melnichenko, *Shakend Nederland* 1980
97	V.Halberstadt, "Themes 64" 1956
98	Raymond Smullyan, 1980
99	T.G.Whitworth, 1987
100	P.A.Lamford, *Chess America* 1981

Chess on the Internet

There are a number of servers that allow chess players to compete online. The ones the author recommends are:

www.freechess.org   FICS - a completely free and popular server

www.chessclub.com   The much acclaimed Internet Chess Club

www.chess.net   Excellent interfaces and top commentary

The first of these is free while the latter two charge an annual fee. In addition you require "gold" membership to get full value from the last named.

Suppliers

There are many hundreds of suppliers of books, software for playing and analysing chess, and magazines. The ones the author recommends, and knows the proprietor personally, are as follows:

British Chess Magazine, 69 Hasbro Road, Kensington, London W14 0LS. Tel: (44) 171 603 2877 Fax: (44) 171 371 1477. Web site at www.bcmchess.co.uk/
Proprietor: GM Murray Chandler

London Chess Centre, 369 Euston Road, London NW1 3AR. Tel: (44) 171 382404 Fax: (44) 171 3882407. Web site at www.chesscenter.com *(note the American spelling of centre).*
Proprietor: IM Malcolm Pein

Inside Chess, P.O.Box 19457, Seattle, WA98109, USA. Tel: 1-800-26-CHESS or (206)286-9764. Fax: (206) 283 4363. Web site at www.insidechess.com
Proprietor: GM Yasser Seirawan.

All the above will send you a catalogue of their products.